:a

Practical Tilapia Fish Pond Farming. All you need

Collins C. Kachaka

Practical Tilapia Fish Pond Farming.
All you Need

LAP LAMBERT Academic Publishing

Imprint

Any brand names and product names mentioned in this book are subject to trademark, brand or patent protection and are trademarks or registered trademarks of their respective holders. The use of brand names, product names, common names, trade names, product descriptions etc. even without a particular marking in this work is in no way to be construed to mean that such names may be regarded as unrestricted in respect of trademark and brand protection legislation and could thus be used by anyone.

Cover image: www.ingimage.com

Publisher:
LAP LAMBERT Academic Publishing
is a trademark of
International Book Market Service Ltd., member of OmniScriptum Publishing Group
17 Meldrum Street, Beau Bassin 71504, Mauritius

Printed at: see last page
ISBN: 978-620-0-53556-6

TABLE CONTENT

APPENDICES

DEDICATION

This special piece of art is dedicated to God Almighty for life, health and the intellectual capacity. He has endowed me with wisdom without which I would not have managed to complete this fish farming revolutionary book. My next profound appreciation goes to my lovely spouse Sombo for her spiritual, physical and emotional support during the tireless nights of writing and research. Thirdly, I would like to appreciate the lovely encouragements and support from my children Kachaka, Masela, Wana, Pezo and Chisambo who have endured the absence of their father's care and presence. **This whole Team believes fish is actually gold.**

ACKNOWLEDGEMENTS

Special acknowledgements go to Mr. Nii Noi Dowuona (Spikes Blog) from Nairobi Kenya who contributed to the content of the book and made it professionally sound and Dr. John Simwiinga from the Department of Literature and Languages University of Zambia who dedicated his precious time to edit and perfect the book through his extraordinary editorial skills.

JUSTIFICATION
Practice Fish Farming Theory!

Admittedly, fish culture in ponds is being practiced all over Zambia and is getting highly popular with many fish farmers attending different forms of theoretical training in fish farming. These training sessions, normally lasting between one and two hours in decorated seminar rooms, take place all around Africa, Zambia inclusive. Up-coming fish farmers have been crowding around these programs in the hope of gaining some knowledge and skills to commence fish farming activities. However, ninety percent of these fish farmers have had to abandon the fish farming activity in utter frustration after encountering enormous challenges resulting in heavy financial losses. According to Kayombo (2017) these challenges include, but are not limited to: lack of comprehensive training packages and materials as well as lack of knowledge in general fish husbandry. They also include lack of capital to improve and increase their investment in aquaculture. These challenges are compounded by low staffing levels in the Ministry of Livestock and Fisheries, which is unable to provide effective extension support.

Most notable of the challenges highlighted above has been lack of technical knowledge to facilitate the effective and successful application of the theoretical knowledge into practice. Theoretical training, though useful in content, lacks the practical aspect which is necessary for one to successfully embark on fish farming. Fish farming training becomes more effective when theory is matched with practice. The book in your palms provides a hands-on step by step approach to fish pond farming. It has been prepared to play a unique supportive role in the improvement of the fish culture management in ponds. This booklet is written based on the experience of fish farmers and describes the methods of fish production using simple techniques and locally available knowledge. Therefore, the booklet should be useful to all who are growing, or intend to grow, tilapia fish as an income-generating venture. It is hoped that by reading this book you will develop a vivid and visual appreciation of what fish pond farming is all about.

The book has been crafted as a self-teaching resource for up-coming fish pond farmers to bridge the yawning gap between theory and practice. This explains why it has been structured in form of a learning module with specific learning outcomes at the beginning of each Chapter. It is our

expectation that after reading each Chapter you should be able to gauge your level of understanding in terms of knowledge, competences and values with regard to pond-fish farming. Even more, we look forward to your putting the knowledge, competences and values attained into actual practice.

"If you are looking for money, then find it in the mouth of the fish. Matthew 17:27"

Chapter One

INTRODUCTION

1.1 Learning Outcomes

By the end of this chapter, you should be able to:

(i) Explain why fish farming is necessary in Zambia;
(ii) Discuss fish farming production methods;
(iii) Illustrate the types of water holding facility in fish farming;
(iv) List the common fish species and their related production systems;
(v) Mention the physical features of a fish pond;
(vi) Show how ponds are categorized according to purpose;
(vii) Illustrate the classification of ponds by construction method, water sources, drainage, construction materials and pond use; and
(viii) Discuss the business opportunities that exist in the fish farming sector.

1.2 Justification for Fish Farming in Zambia

Scanning the Zambian ecosystem, one is hypnotized by the phenomenon of many natural water bodies (rivers, canals, streams and lakes) spread across the country in the midst of poverty-stricken, depressed, misery-laden communities camped around in two meter high structures. These people usually lament the fast dwindling amounts of fish in the natural water bodies and, ironically, often angrily appeal to the government not to impose fish bans. Fish in these water bodies has been depleted by these unscrupulous fishermen using unorthodox fishing methods, which eliminate even the young fish.

The current national annual fish requirement for the country is staggering at 120,000 tons but only about 70,000 tons is supplied leaving 50,000 tons which is supplied through imports (Shula and Mukuka, 2015). With increased urban population now growing at the rate of 2.3 percent (CSO, 2012), the demand for fish has tremendously grown. Zambia has been importing fish for culture and for consumption since 1980's (FAO, 2006). Additionally, Musuka et al, (2017) have stated that the country imports between 4,626 and 16,077 tons of fish annually from neighboring countries such as Zimbabwe, Mozambique and Namibia. One of the most sustainable solutions to this seemingly endless shortage of fish lies in fish farming. Fish farming entails creating production fish ponds where fish can be nurtured and controlled for better growth and harvest. Fish ponds need to be scaled up in order to meet the demand for fish and fish products as well as to eliminate the poverty syndrome in a country which is endowed with plenty of both surface and underground water resources. Fish ponds can be dug around these natural water bodies in every village thereby eliminating the currently stinging poverty. Water can be diverted from the natural water bodies into the ponds and closed when necessary for fish culturing. Fish ponds have been known to eliminate rural poverty in Bangladeshi, Kenya and China (Karki, 2016). A fish pond campaign needs to be launched so that every village, church, community and company owns its own fish pond for the betterment of Zambia's economy. Arising from the significant economic value of fish farming, the Chinese call it 'fish gold'. This gold has been with us for years and we have not benefited from it. Arise and dig.

1.3 What Does Fish Farming Involve?

1.3.1 Definition and objective

The term 'fish farming' involves all forms of culture of aquatic animals and plants in fresh-brackish and saltwater. Fish farming has the same objective as agriculture: to increase the production of fish for food above the level which would be produced naturally. **As in agriculture, fish farming techniques includes:**

- the removal of unwanted plants and animals and replacing them with desirable species,
- the improvement of these species by cross-breeding and selection, and
- the improvement of food availability by the use of fertilizers.

Fish farming can be combined with agriculture, animal husbandry and irrigation practices which can lead to better utilization of local resources and ultimately higher production and net profits. Fish farming production methods vary widely and differ in the intensity of culturing technique employed; the level of water exchange and the structures which have been used. Each method has its own set of benefits and challenges.

1.3.2 Fish farming production methods

Fish farming production methods can be broadly grouped into three intensities:

Extensive - This uses large stagnant ponds that allow only a low stocking density and rely on natural production to feed the fish (i.e. there is no supplemental feeding). Management and skills input is low.

Semi-Intensive - This is much like extensive production culture method, however there is a greater degree of intervention either through feeding and/or improvement of water quality through aeration and partial water exchange. This allows for an increase in the production of fish when compared to the extensive production culture method. Management and skills input occur at a medium level.

Intensive - Utilizing the intensive culturing method of production enables the fish farmer to maintain high stocking densities and feeding comes solely from introduced feeds. The intensive culturing method of production tends to be highly technical and rely on electricity to operate. The space required is relatively small and the system is designed to optimize water use and quality. In countries, where climatic factors are against the year-round production of warm water fish species, the intensive culturing method of production enables farmers to utilize greenhouses for a year round production cycles. Management and skills input are high.

1.3.3   Water holding facility

The production method used in fish farming depends on the type of water holding facility in which the fish are grown. **Water holding facilities are classified into:**

Pond culture - Ponds can be earthen or concrete, but most of the production takes place in earthen ponds. Ponds vary in sizes and range from about a quarter acre to several acres. Fish production may take place in a farm pond or in ponds specifically designed and constructed for aquaculture. Though most farm ponds have fish growing in them, they may not be suitable for commercial aquaculture because, quite often, they have uncertain water quality and uneven water depths and do not have a drainage system. However, many farm ponds have been used to produce fish in cages and in recreational or fee fishing operations. Ponds specifically designed and constructed for fish culture require some amount of clay soils to retain water. Ponds that are less than 2 acres are recommended because they are less difficult to manage than larger ones.

Cage culture - Cage culture involves producing fish in floating cages in lakes, dams or ponds, allowing water to flow freely between the fish and the pond, dam or lake. Cage culture is similar to pond culture, except that fish are enclosed in cages and not swimming freely like in the pond. One major advantage is the convenience of harvesting fish, especially where the pond, dam or lake is too deep for seining. Cages vary in shape and size, and can be rectangular, square, or round. The cage size depends on the size of the pond, dam or lake, availability of aeration, and the method of harvest. Larger cages are difficult to handle during harvesting. Manufactured cages are commonly sold as 4x4 feet (diameter x depth) cylindrical cages, 4 x 4 x 4 feet and 8 x 8 x 4 feet (length x width x depth) square cages, and 8 x 4 x 4 feet and 12 x 6 x 4 feet rectangular cages. The cages must be placed in open areas of the pond, dam or lake with at least 2 feet of water between the bottom of the cage and the pond bottom, allowing adequate water circulation to supply needed oxygen in and around the cages.

Raceway culture - Culture systems where water moves or flows through channels at relatively high rates are commonly called "raceways" or "flow through" systems. The channels can be ponds or in ground or above ground tanks constructed with concrete, tile, brick, wood, etc. They are arranged in a series of terraced raceways to allow water to flow by gravity through each unit. The feature that distinguishes raceways from ponds is the flow through, so raceways generally, require large volumes of good quality water to flow through the units. Water sources for raceways are normally obtained from a spring, creek, or stream and channeled through the raceways by gravity. Water can be pumped back (recirculated) to flow through the units, but this can result in a very expensive operation. The water flow through the raceways removes fish wastes from the units, and at the same time the water is replenished with oxygen as it spills into the next raceway along the terrace. Most raceway culture occurs where there are high volumes of spring water for the production of Coldwater species such as trout.

Water recirculating systems – Simple recirculating systems for aquaculture production consist of (a) a tank for holding the fish, (b) a solid waste removal system for removing solid fish waste and uneaten feed, (c) a biofilter for removing dissolved toxic wastes, (d) an aerator to supply oxygen, and (e) a pump to recirculate the water. Other components can be added to recirculating systems to make them more efficient, but they also add additional complexity. Because the systems involve recirculating the water used, relatively less water is needed for this type of culture system compared to pond culture or raceway/flow through systems. Fish production requires attention to critical factors such as water temperature, concentrations of dissolved oxygen, unionized ammonia nitrogen, nitrite concentration, pH, and alkalinity levels. Most of the recirculating systems are placed indoors to allow the famer to maintain control over these critical factors to ensure good water quality during the growing period. Recirculating aquaculture systems are capital intensive and require close monitoring of the growing conditions of the fish, but they also allow for year round control of growing conditions. Therefore, farmers interested in this type of production system should begin on a small scale before expanding into large scale production system. Not all fish grow well in all of these facilities. Some do better than others in particular facilities. Table 1 provides a list of species suitable for culturing and the common production system to use:

Table 1 Common fish species and production Systems

Species	Common Production System
Bluegill	Ponds, Recirculating system
Catfish	Ponds, Recirculating system, Cages
Fathead minnows	Ponds, Recirculating system
Tilapia	**Ponds, Cages, Recirculating system**
Freshwater Prawn	Ponds
Goldfish	Ponds, Recirculating system
Golden Shiner	Ponds, Recirculating system
Hybrid Striped Bass	Ponds, Cages, Recirculating system
Largemouth Bass	Ponds
Rainbow Trout	Raceways/Flow through system, Ponds, Cages
Smallmouth Bass	Ponds
Walleye	Ponds
Yellow Perch	Ponds, Recirculating system

1.4   Fish Farming Using Ponds

With the explicit depletion of the fish species in most of our water bodies and the continual negative effects of climate change on our aquatic ecosystem, fish culture utilizing ponds has become one of the most feasible and sustainable source of fish. Under extensive fish farming, we mainly have earthen ponds, semi-intensive fish farming may include earthen ponds and cages while intensive fish farming has cages, raceways, tanks, earthen and concrete fish ponds to mention but a few (Genschick et al.,2017).

Fish production utilizing earth ponds requires fresh water, and the pond should be able to accommodate the storage, farming, and harvest of fish. Construction of the ponds and associated structures require specific preparations and tasks, which are essential for success. Moreover, the ponds must be inexpensive to build, easy to maintain, and tidy to ensure that the water and the fish are managed well. A fish pond is a shallow body of water, used for the controlled farming of fish. It is adapted to be easily and completely drained. It includes:

- A plate that forms the bottom of the pond.
- Dikes, which surround the pond and form walls that contain the water. These walls must be solid, to resist water pressure, and impermeable.
- An intake structure that collects water to fill the pond.
- The emissary, a river or canal that allows for drainage.
- Canals that bring or evacuate pond water: the supply canal or water inlet brings collected water to the pond. The draining canal or evacuation allows drainage toward the emissary.
- Regulation devices control the water's level, flow, or both: the water inlet is the device that regulates water flowing toward the pond and stops water from flooding. The water outlet, preferably a monk, controls the water level and evacuation of the pond.
- The outfall or overflow allows evacuation of excess water, ensuring safety.
- Filters, if necessary, prevent animals and particles from entering or exiting the pond
- A fence surrounds the pond and keeps undesirable visitors out.
- Other structures provide protection against fish-eating birds, if necessary.
- Access ways and roads surround the pond and allow people to reach it.

Piscicultural fresh water ponds differ by the origin of their water supply, their drainage method, construction materials and processes, and, finally, fish farming methods. These characteristics are usually determined by the characteristics of the site where they are built. Concerning the utilization of a pond, the same pond can serve different purposes, depending on the specific moment and the evolution of the installation. One will find:

- Spawning ponds for production of eggs and small fry;
- Nursery ponds for production of larger juveniles;
- Brood ponds for rearing brood stock;
- Storage ponds for holding fish temporarily, often before they are sold;
- Fattening ponds, for the production of fish that will be consumed;
- Integrated ponds that include crops, animals or other fish ponds, which supply waste materials that act as feed or fertilizer for the pond.

1.5   Classification of fish ponds

According to Omofunmi (2016), there are a number of ways to classify fish ponds. Fish ponds can be classified according to the construction method, water sources, drainage, construction materials and pond use. In terms of design and construction, ponds can be classified in two groups, namely; embankment and excavated ponds. Embankment ponds impound water primarily above the ground level. This type of pond is best suited to sloping locations. Surface water is usually relied on to fill these ponds while Excavated (Sunken or Dug out) ponds are excavated or dug out into the soil so that water is impounded primarily below ground level. Such ponds normally are constructed on relatively flat lands where embankment ponds would be impractical. Either surface water or ground water seepage fills the excavated reservoir. Pumped water can be used as a primary or supplemental source of water for either pond type. However, because of the expenses involved, it is usually best to choose a site where pumping can be minimized if not avoided altogether. Successful construction of either type of pond depends on the capacity of the soils in the reservoir area to hold water and to provide stable side-slope and dikes. Sites must, therefore, be carefully selected.

Accordingly, ponds can also be classified according to water sources. In this case we can have spring water ponds and seepage ponds which generally receive their water from the ground. Ponds which receive their water from rain are called rain-fed while those that get their water from water bodies like dams, streams, lakes are called barrage ponds. These ponds are normally fed by water directly running from the water body or by water entering a channel from which controlled amounts can be fed to the pond. Other ponds in this category include pump-fed ponds. Okoma and Ezenwa (2001) further explain that ponds can also be classified according to drainage. In this case we have undrainable and drainable ponds. Undrainable ponds are those which cannot be drained by gravity while the opposite is true for drainable ponds. Drainable ponds are normally constructed at a level higher than the level at which water is drained. In this class we also have pump drained ponds which heavily rely on pumping out water but can to some extent be drained by gravity as well.

Generally, most people describe fish ponds as earthen (Fig. 1), walled and lined ponds (Fig. 2). This classification is primarily based on construction materials. Earthen ponds are primarily made from soil materials usually from clay-type soil because of its capacity to retain water. On the other hand, walled ponds are those constructed from blocks and concrete, though sometimes wooden planks are also employed. Lined ponds are basically earthen ponds which make use of impervious materials such as plastic dam liners in order to control seepage and manage water levels. Ponds can also be classified according to the usage. In this category, we have brood stock ponds which are used for propagation of the new generation of fish. Brood stock or brood fish, are a group of mature **individuals** used in aquaculture for breeding purposes. Brood stock can be a population of animals maintained in captivity as a source of replacement for, or enhancement of, seed and fry numbers (Waples and Do, 1994). Fattening or grow-out ponds are used for raising fingerlings to market size. These usually have a large surface area while Nursery ponds manage fingerlings in the early stages before they are sold for further fattening. Storage or holding fish ponds help to temporarily keep the fish before it is offloaded to the market

Figure 1 *Earthen pond*

Figure 2 *lined pond*

1.6 Business Opportunities in the Fish Farming Sector

Fish farming is not only practiced for domestic use but also for job creation and economic value. Fish farming business is the creation of economic value from fish, fish products and its environment. There are a number of businesses that can be opened up from fish farming activities.

1.6.1 *Fingerling Business*

Fingerlings are tiny fish, which constitute fish seed. Fingerlings are required for fish farming and the preservation of fish species especially with many species already extinct. The sustainability of fish farming solely depends upon the ready availability of fingerlings, therefore venturing into fingerling culturing and production is a very lucrative business. In order to undertake this business, the farmer will need to thoroughly understand the popular fish species on the market. This business, though very lucrative requires some minimal initial capital investments in basic technology for the management of the fingerlings which normally mature in 21 days depending on the species. Small-scale fish farmers can actually breed fingerlings if they have the necessary technical know-how. In Zambia, fingerlings are currently sold between thirty to sixty ngwee per fingerling and they range from 1 to 10grams. As of the year 2018, Palabana Fisheries and First Hatch sold fingerlings at forty (K0.40) ngwee each while Savanna Streams limited, Horizon Aquaculture limited and IBAN Aquaculture Solutions sold at fifty (K0.50) ngwee each. Fingerlings are a huge business in Zambia. Genschick et al. (2017) state that there is a shortage of fingerlings in the country. In 2015, the six operating state-run hatcheries in the country produced only 516,000 fingerlings (mostly O. macrochir, T. rendalli and O. andersonii). This quantity was not enough to meet the fingerling demand of over 12,000 registered fish farmers around the country.

1.6.2 *Sell of Dam Liners*

Some fish farmers have argued that, the most expensive component of fish farming is the purchase of dam liners. Pond dam liners are hardened polythene plastics that are used for holding water to prevent seepage in dams and ponds. Pond liners are very important in fish farming especially in soils that do not have water retention capacity. Most of the soils, apart from those in river plains (clay), do not have water retaining properties and will, therefore, need pond liners in order to construct fish ponds. Pond liners are therefore a critical element of fish pond farming ecosystem. Zambia does not have a factory for manufacturing pond liners and therefore this becomes a very lucrative business if ventured upon. Many farmers normally endure 6-8 frustrating months waiting for pond liners from China to arrive from few resellers around the country. Zambia needs approximately Ten (10) Pond Liner Suppliers per province in order to satisfy the market. As of 2018, a typical 500micron x 100m x 7m Pond Liner costed between K14, 500 and K35,000 depending on the source. One Pond Liner Entrepreneur stated that he sold, on average, 20 Pond Liners per day. Pond liners are measured by their level of thickness in millimeters (mm) or microns. Pond liner specifications usually take the form of Thickness x Length x Width where the length and width are measured in meters (m). According to Peggs (2003) durability of the pond liners is a function of its thickness. The thicker the pond liner, the more durable it is. For more information on pond liners, refer to chapter 3.

1.6.3 *Fishing Sports Business*

Many people like having fun and relaxation around water thereby bringing in water sports as a business. Water plays a pivotal role in balancing body temperatures and nourishing the brain as well as helping in deep thoughts. I therefore define Fishing Sports as fish catching entertainments that involve an individual, a group or family. Fishing sports in the pond become very successful because of the easy availability of fish. River fishing sports are tough and labor-intensive owing to the fact that catching fish is not easy. Most often fishermen have gone home frustrated with their money lost in the expedition without any fish caught. In a pond, this is not the case because everyone is assured of making a catch thus enjoying the sport. Most often, fishing sports where fish are caught, employ a hook. People line up along the fish pond normally with music playing; sometimes with song and dance while catching fish through the hook. This business is good because people pay for registration as well as for each fish caught. Normally the price of fresh fish caught in this manner is three-times more expensive that the ordinary one on the market thus making it more lucrative as a business. However, downsizing to this is that injured fish may die within few hours or may cause pond disease that may spread to other fish. The fish farmer needs to make sure that the fish that seems to be swimming on the surface after the fishing sport expedition is treated in coarse salt or removed altogether. Additionally, fishing sports need to be done only in a designated fish pond or reservoir specifically designated for such, not in all.

1.6.4   *Fresh Fish Sales*

Fresh fish sales constitute the most common business that fish farmers are engaged in. The business can be carried out at wholesale or retail depending on the scale of the business. According to a recently conducted fish value chain report by ILO (2014) Zambia has an estimated current fish supply deficit of 57,000 metric tons. Fish is a delicacy in most homes around the country and makes very good business. The current wholesale and retail prices (as of the year 2018) range from K25.00 - K27.00 and K30.00 - K42.00 per kilogram respectively depending on the source and the season.

1.6.5   *Dry Fish Sales*

Selling of dry fish is another very lucrative business that one may undertake. This is because dry fish is four times more expensive than fresh fish. Nonetheless, dry fish requires careful management in order to preserve it for the market. A big drying oven or smoking kilns may be required in cold weather to mitigate the dimming sunshine. Salting as a preservative is also required as well as sacks for proper storage. In the recent years, dry fish has been fetching between K50.00 and K80.00 for three pieces of dried fish. Additionally, dry fish may be transported to the Democratic Republic of Congo where three pieces of dried fish are going at K150.00. Many people fear to venture into dry fish business because of the labor involved in managing the fish before its ready for the market.

1.6.6   *Cold Vehicles Fish Transportation*

Another important line of fish business, though not popular in Zambia, is cold-room fish transportation. This involves having a fleet of cold-room vehicles that help in transporting the fish on behalf of farmers from the ponds to the market, especially where there is long distance to the market and huge quantities of fish. One can buy a cold-room truck from Japan and use it to help fish farmers ferry fish to the market. Some fish farmers have lamentably seen their fish rot as a result of not having quick transport to the market. This business, will however, need to be marketed in the fish farmers network.

1.6.7   *Fish Product Processing Business*

Processing of fish to create other fish products is yet another intriguing business. This business requires huge investments because it involves establishing a factory mostly near to a sustainable fish source. Owing to the fact that the demand for fish in Zambia is greater than the supply, this business is carried out on a subsistence level and comes from the residue that remains from the sun- drying of fish (ZDA, 2011). It is expected that with increased production, more processed fish products will be on the market. Processed fish products include fish cakes, fish powder and the famous tinned fish.

1.6.8   *Fish Pond Construction*

With the escalating demand for fish in most of the urban cities and diminishing returns from crop agriculture, many farmers are turning to fish farming. This is because fish farming can be carried out even in land that is depleted of its nutrients. Farmers can still obtain significant value from such land where crops have ceased to grow. Pond construction is the art of creating ponds on a designated piece of land usually by digging. Pond construction is labor-intensive and makes most of the farmers too lazy to galvanize enough energy to venture into it. Therefore, specializing in fish pond construction can be a very rewarding activity. This is the case because farmers get discouraged from self-constructing ponds using the traditional shovel and wheelbarrow method because it takes too long just to construct one pond. Depending on the size of the pond, using the traditional method may take about four to five days to construct a 30m x 10m pond with 10 dedicated men. Venturing into this business may therefore require you to buy an excavator (even a second hand one from Japan) and rely on it for fish pond excavation. An excavator may dig 3 to 4 fish ponds a day depending on size and soil formation. The current rates (as of the year 2018) are K800 or (us$ 70) per hour and translate into Six Thousand Four Hundred (K6,400) Kwacha or us$ 535 in 8 hours.

The best approach would be to sensitize fish farmers in various locations of the impeding visit by the excavator. For example, farmers in Mazabuka can be sensitized and registered in 1-3 weeks period. The excavator would then be sent in the area to camp and dig ponds for the registered farmers. Farmers who intend to venture into this business need to design workable business models that may incorporate various factors which include distances to be covered to the various farms, size of the ponds to be excavated, complexity of the soil structure, time spent on excavation, fuel and required depth among others.

1.6.9   *Manufacture and Selling Fish Feed*

With increased number of fish farmers, there is critical need for more fish feed on the market. According to a report by Genschick et al. (2017), Zambia has a total of 12,010 registered Small Scale Fish farmers. With increased numbers of small scale fish farmers, the business of fish feed becomes lucrative because fish farmers will need feed for their ponds. Despite the fact that local traditional feeds are effective in successfully managing fish ponds, some fish farmers will still need commercial feeds for supplementation purposes. Additionally, some farmers may not have the time to manufacture their own fish feed through feed formulation. These farmers may rely on traditional feed like mixtures of sunflower meal, maize bran and moringa or as the case maybe fresh duck and chicken manure. In these circumstances, fish will still grow steadily and healthy especially where the pond is well fertilized and not overstocked.

Fish feed business comes in two forms:-

(a)   Manufacturing and processing of fish feed: This business requires some investment in machinery and equipment. This is much more applicable for large scale investments. This machinery is necessary for mixing and optimizing the raw materials into various grades (types) of fish feed to meet various fish age categories. Farmers and cooperatives can then directly buy for their final use. Nevertheless, Small Scale Fish Farmers can still make their own fish feed using small hand mincers and traditional mortars.

(b)   Re-selling of fish feed: This is yet another lucrative and easy business. Depending on the number of fish farmers in your locality, you can engage in this business such that you can be ordering feed on wholesale prices and then retail it. This will shorten the distance for farmers in acquiring feed.

1.7 Check your progress

In 1.1 we stated that by the end of this chapter, you should be able to:

(i)   Explain why fish farming is necessary in Zambia;

(ii)   Discuss fish farming production methods;

(iii)   Illustrate the types of water holding facility in fish farming;

(iv)   List the common fish species and their related production systems;

(v)   Mention the physical features of a fish pond;

(vi)   Show how ponds are categorized according to purpose;

(vii)   Illustrate the classification of ponds by construction method, water sources, drainage, construction materials and pond use; and

(viii) Discuss the business opportunities that exist in the fish farming sector.

Now set the booklet aside and test yourself on how many of the outcomes you have achieved.

Chapter Two

POND CITING AND CONSTRUCTION

2.1 Learning Outcomes

By the end of this chapter, you should be able to:

(i)   Discuss the critical factors to consider when pond siting;
(ii)   Outline the steps involved in fish pond excavation;
(iii)   Explain each of the steps involved in fish pond excavation; and
(iv)   Correctly construct a fish pond.

2.2. Pond Siting

When thinking of constructing a fish pond, it is very important to make a careful intelligent plan especially when citing. I define pond siting as an exercise to determine a suitable location for the pond. This is very important because random digging may be very costly and time consuming. The most critical success factors to consider when carrying out pond siting are land topography (type of land), water source, water quality, soil type, proximity to people and the road for safety and accessibility. Additionally, construction of a pond must carefully take into account economic factors so as to construct a pond within ones sustainable budget.

2.2.1 *Land topography*

This factor is crucial because it determines whether or not the pond will be successfully constructed. Land topography refers to the shape and features of the land in question. Rocky and stony land may not be suitable for a fish pond because digging may pose a serious challenge. Typically sloppy land may also not be very good for a pond because of soil erosions and landslides during the rainy season which may swamp and wash away the pond unless careful planning and construction is made. Flat land is highly recommended for fish ponds because it is easier to dig.

2.2.2 *Water source*

This is yet another very important factor to consider when citing a pond. The surveyor needs to determine whether there is a good water source (river, stream, spring) within 100 to 200m of the pond. Additionally, the surveyor needs to check whether the water table is close to the soil surface or not. This may necessitate the digging of a well-watered borehole to supply enough water to the pond. Water engineers may be required to ascertain the quality and quality of underground water resources. A sustainable water source is imperative in fish culture, as it is a precursor for good water quality.

According to Ngueku (2014), there are two main sources of water to the ponds. These are ground water and surface water. Ground water comprises springs and wells or boreholes while surface water comes from rain and run-off water, natural water course, irrigation canals and drainage canals.

Ground water supplies are reliable as they have their source from aquifers lying at different depths. This ground water is sourced from boreholes and natural water courses with the latter being preferred on account of its being less costly than former. Both borehole construction and pumping are costly. Details of water quantity and quality are dealt with in chapter five.

2.2.3   *Trees*
Farmers constructing fish ponds are advised not to put them in areas where shade from trees covers the pond. Ponds are required to be placed in direct sunlight so as to allow for phytoplankton and algae to carry out photosynthesis which is necessary for the production of dissolved oxygen needed by the fish. Leaves from trees also affect the suitability of ponds in that once they fall into the pond they prevent the passage of adequate sunlight required for the optimum growth of the fish.

2.2.4   *Soil Type*
The type of soil is a very crucial factor because it determines the amount of investment that will be required to make the pond a success. A good experiment usually involves holding the soil in the hand and then letting it down. If the soil is easily blown off by the wind, then it is not very ideal and you may need investment in pond liners in order to make a pond. This means your soil does not have water retention capabilities. However, if the soil is clay (Fig. 3), then the pond will be less costly because concrete and pond liners will not be necessary.

Figure 3 Clay soil Source. (www.shutterstock.com 2018).

2.2.5   *Soil Chemistry*

The chemistry of the soil is another very important element that needs to be seriously considered.   This is because the quality of the water in the fish ponds will largely depend on the chemistry of the soil. In this regard, you are required to measure the pH of the soil to determine whether the soils are alkaline, neutral or acidic. Of importance is to look at the extent of alkalinity or acidity. Both alkaline and acidic soils are not good for fish ponds but intervening mechanisms can be put in place to control the extremes. A layman's experiment will just involve ascertaining whether or not crop yield is optimum in such soil. If crops do well in this soil, then it may be good for a pond. Other chemical elements like water hardness, amount of nitrates can also be looked at.

2.2.6   *Proximity to People and the Road*

It is important that the pond is sited as close as possible to home so as to avert fish theft as well as to improve pond security and management. Ponds are susceptible to predators and human intruders. The nearness to home is important for easy accessibility in order to constantly monitor fish behaviour and activate various interventions. Additionally, road accessibility is important for easy transportation of fish feed to the farm and ferrying fish to the market.

2.2.7 *Land ownership*

In order to avoid wrangles, land ownership needs to be clearly ascertained or proper officially documented authorization for a particular period needs to be obtained before pond construction can commence in order to avoid loss of investment.

2.3 Fish Pond Excavation

With regard to constructing high-quality ponds, construction work should follow specific steps in a strict order. The general steps for any type of pond include:-

(i)   Planning pond layout;
(ii)   Cleaning of the site;
(iii)   Water supply channel designing;
(iv)   Draining channel designing;
(v)   Staking out the pond;
(vi)   Building the dikes;
(vii)   Pond bottom drain laying out;
(viii)   Building inlet, outlet and filtration;
(ix)   Other structures: Erosion fight, biological plastic, fence; and
(x)   Filling and testing.

Technical aspects for the step by step pond construction will not be detailed in this manual because these are demonstrated during actual construction. During pond excavation, the farmer might have to employ strong community men in the case of a small fish pond but if it is a large pond, then an excavator may need to be hired. The very first activity is to clear off the grass and leaves on the selected site after which the farmer will need to measure the length and width of the fish pond and place the required number of pegs (usually eight) accordingly around a rope. The fish farmer must ensure that the deeper side of the pond is 40% of the pond total length while the other 60% is divided in half to cover the middle and shallower sides. Actual digging and slopping can then start. The dugout soil should be carefully harnessed to create dykes, which normally extend several meters above the pond. The digging is required to cascade from the shallower side to the deeper one. Plant some grass on the dykes to make them stronger and protect them from collapsing due to soil erosion. This is called turfing. The grass prevents the dykes from being swept away by rain water during the rainy season. Additionally, dykes help to prevent soil pouring into the fish pond during windy days. Soil may stick into the gills of the fish thus preventing respiration and resulting in death. In order to strengthen the dykes, spray some water and compact the soil. The deeper side of the pond should be at least 2m deep (though 1.5m is also acceptable) while the shallower side can be 0.5m deep even though others maintain it at 1m. Care must be taken not to increase the pond depth beyond 2m because it will prevent sunlight from reaching the bottom of the pond. This may create sections and stratification inside the pond, which is undesirable. Do not use loose soils or rocks to create dykes because they may not be strong enough to prevent water leakages. Technical details of pond measurement and construction are demonstrated in practice during training.

Outlet pipes can then be constructed usually at the deeper end of the pond because of the existence of pressure. Four-inch sewer pipes usually six meters long are used for this purpose. The outlet pipes are very important in helping to drain water cheaply and easily during harvesting. This entails that within few hours, the harvest activity is completed. Draining water through the outlet pipes is also an integral part of pond management when the water is too contaminated. Additionally, the inlet and outlet pipes help control pond flooding during rainy season. The sewer pipe is required to be at the required height just above the water level but not too high because during floods, as the water rises, the pond may flood allowing the fish to flow out with the water. Therefore, the sewer pipe requires being at the optimum height just slightly above the water level but below the pond height. This is important because fish pond flooding will be prevented thus keeping the fish in the pond

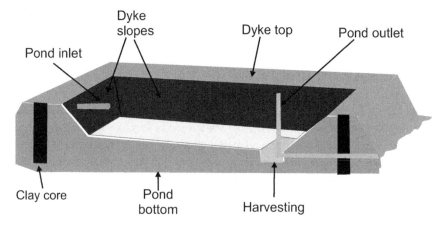

Figure 4 Cross section of a typical earthen fishpond. Source: FAO (2004

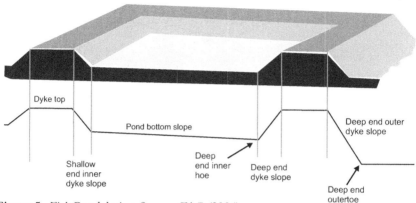

Figure 5 Fish Pond design. Source: FAO (2004)

2.4   Check Your Progress

In 2.1we stated that by the end of this chapter, you should be able to:

(i)   Discuss the critical factors to consider when pond siting;

(ii)   Outline the steps involved in fish pond excavation;

(iii)   Explain each of the steps involved in fish pond excavation; and

(iv)   Correctly construct a fish pond.

Now set the booklet aside and test yourself on how many of the outcomes you have achieved.

Chapter Three

POND LINERS

3.1   Learning Outcomes

By the end of this chapter, you should be able to:

(i)   Use the standard formula to calculate the required length of a pond liner;

(ii)   Discuss the critical factors to consider when selecting pond liners;

(iii)   List some common pond liner sizes on the Zambian market;

(iv)   Explain the procedure for joining pond liners;

(v)   Correctly join pond liners.

3.2   What are Pond Liners?

Pond liners are thick and hardened virgin high-density polyethylene resin plastics needed for insertion in a pond where soils cannot retain water. Dam liners come in various sizes and dimensions. Considering the fact that fish ponds are of different dimensions and shapes, pond liners need to be joined together in order to meet the pond size and shape. The first step when measuring the pond is to find the deepest point and measure the depth. This is done by placing a board across the deeper point from end to end and measuring upwards at that point. Afterwards, measure the length and width of the pond if it was not already measured. According to Celeste *et al.* (2014), the formula for calculating the correct length for a pond liner is: **length + twice the depth + 0.6m** Likewise the pond width will be **width + twice the depth + 0.6m** Doubling the depth accounts for lining the inside of the pond and the 0.6m allows for an overlap on either side. Therefore, if the fish pond is 50m long by 25m wide with a depth of 2m, the pond liner size needed to fit in the pond without any further adjustments would then be 54.6m x 29.6m. For a 30m x 10m pond size, calculate the right size of the pond liner necessary to line this pond. A pond liner of exactly the same size as the fish pond will not fit into the pond.

Fish farmers can also purchase pond liner rolls which are then joined and fitted into the pond. In this case, the farmer needs to calculate the correct number of pond liner rolls required to line his pond. The formula here is Area of the Pond liner divide by the area of the fish pond plus twice the average depth, which covers the inside of the pond. The answer you get needs to be rounded off to the nearest whole number.

3.3   Pond Liner Sizes

Pond liners come in various sizes and thickness (Table 2). Normally pond liner thickness is measured in microns (μ) or millimeters (mm) while the length and width are measured in meters (m). Pond liners come in various colors and their width range from 1meter to 8meters while their lengths are determined by the buyer. Standard length may go up to 200m, thickness ranges from 0.2mm (200microns) up to 1mm (1000microns) as can be seen in Table 2

Table 2 Various pond liner thicknesses and durability

Millimeters	Microns	Order of Durability
0.25mm	(250microns)	
0.3mm	(300microns)	
0.4mm	(400microns)	
0.5mm	(500microns)	
0.75mm	(750microns)	
1mm	(1000microns)	

Some common pond liner sizes on the Zambian market include 500microns x 100m x 7m; 500microns x 100m x 6m; 250microns x 50m x 6m; 300microns x 50m x 3m; 250microns x 30m x 3m. Most of the Zambian fish farmers use 500 micron thick pond liners because of their durability.

3.4   Pond Liner Selection

The following factors are critical in deciding on the type of pond liners:-

(a)   Funds;

(b)   Availability; and

(c)   Type and duration of fish project.

Nevertheless, the thicker the pond liner, the more expensive it is and the longer the durability. Pond liners need to be spread inside the excavated fish pond where the joining will take place. This is good because it saves the farmer the hustle of pulling the pond liners from where they have been assembled into the pond. Additionally and more importantly, joining the pond liners inside the pond helps in measuring the required dimensions to meet pond requirements because very often fish farmers miscalculate the dimensions of pond liners. The miscalculations arise because they do not take into account the depth of the pond. They only look at the length and the width. Joining pond liners requires very specialized skill otherwise the pond liners will be damaged resulting in costly losses.

3.5   How to Join Pond Liners

Most of the fish farmers have been joining dam liners with a pressing iron. This is not the professional way of doing it because the hot iron sticks to the pond liners and creates holes. Furthermore, the joined pieces sometimes leave spaces, which allow water to seep during water filling. The professional method of joining pond liners is to use **Ponder Liner Welder** (as shown in Fig. 6). The pond liner welding machine is a specialized tool that puts together pond liners without much stress. It moves on its own line by line until the liners are fully joined. Nevertheless, some pond liner welding skills are required in order to effectively use the welder. A short course of three hours is sufficient to master the technique of using the pond liner welder. This skill is also offered during the hands-on training.

Figure 6 Pond liner welder. Source: Breathing Fish Farm (2018)

In addition, you will need a Pond Liner Gun (as shown in Figure 7). This is yet another important tool required to complete the installation and configuration of the pond liners. Its role is to seal or patch holes, which may have arisen as a result of packing from the factory. These holes must be sealed so as to prevent the seepage of water from the pond. The Pond Liner Gun requires some technical skill for effective usage.

Figure 7 Pond liner Gun. Source: Breathing Fish Farm (2018)

3.6 Check your Progress

In 3.1 we stated that by the end of this chapter, you should be able to:
- (i) Use the standard formula to calculate the required length of a pond liner;
- (ii) Discuss the critical factors to consider when selecting pond liners;
- (iii) List some common pond liner sizes on the Zambian market;
- (iv) Explain the procedure for joining pond liners;
- (v) Correctly join pond liners.

Now set the booklet aside and test yourself on how many of these outcomes you have achieved.

Chapter Four

POND FERTILIZATION

4.1   Learning Outcomes

By the end of this chapter, you should be able to:

(i)   Define pond fertilization;

(ii)   Explain the requirements for the maintenance of an optimum plankton bloom;

(iii)   Outline the procedure for pond fertilization;

(iv)   Discuss the advantages and disadvantages of organic fertilizers and animal fertilizers;

(v)   Recall the application rates for different types of fertilizer;

(vi)   Correctly fertilize a fish pond.

4.2   What is pond fertilization?

Pond fertilization is the phenomenon of adding chemicals or organic fertilizers to the pond water in order to create a live water body suitable for fish growth and survival. This process needs to be undertaken immediately after water has been filled in the pond but one to two weeks before fingerling stocking. Fertilized pond water changes into slight greenish color. The greenish color is an indicator of the presence of algae and other aquatic organic substances predominantly phytoplankton.

It is common knowledge that the clear natural water used to fill the pond does not contain food for fish. Pond water is like agricultural land: if the ground is fertile, the plants grow well. To make water fertile, fertilizing elements, particularly phosphorus, must be added. Water will respond much more readily to fertilization if its physical and chemical characteristics (temperature, pH, dissolved oxygen, etc.) are close to the optimal ranges for selected species. Fertilization increases the production of natural food in a pond, making it possible for fish to find more food. Fertilization provides food for the living organisms that then provide food for fish. When manure is used to increase fish production in ponds, it will establish and maintain a dense population of phytoplankton and zooplankton, which should turn the water into a beautiful green colour. Most of the time, fish will eat small animals and plants that grow in green water. However, it may be necessary to provide additional food if primary production in the pond is not optimum and the fish grow slowly.

Nutritionally, organic matter includes proteins, lipids (fats), and carbohydrates, as well as substances present in relatively low proportions (micronutrients), such as vitamins and minerals. Nutritional requirements vary by species.

Fertilizers are natural or synthetic substances that are used in ponds to increase the production of the natural food organisms to be eaten by the fish. These organisms include phytoplankton, zooplankton and insects. They are all part of a complex food chain necessary for fish growth. By increasing the availability of major nutrients, fertilizers promote the development of planktonic algae, which provide food for many fish.

According to FAO (2003), when using fertilizers to increase fish production in your ponds, you should aim to establish and maintain a dense growth of planktonic algae (phytoplankton) and zooplankton, which should color the water a rich shade of green. Such dense planktonic growth is often called a plankton bloom. In order to establish and maintain an optimum plankton bloom, the farmer needs to ensure the following:-

- Pond water and bottom soil should be neutral or slightly alkaline, lime the water if necessary;
- Control the immersed vegetation and the mud thickness, if possible by draining;
- Reduce the competition for nutrients and sunlight by controlling the floating and submersed vegetation;
- Reduce the water exchange rate as much as possible to avoid draining away water rich in nutrients and plankton;
- Fertilize each pond according to its particular characteristics; for example, use more fertilizer if the pond is new, and appropriate mud has not yet formed;
- Use more fertilizer if the water supply is poor in nutrients; and
- Use more fertilizer if the bottom soil is sandy rather than clay.

4.3   How is pond fertilization done?

FAO (2003) explains that fish ponds are usually fertilized by use of a combination of Urea and Phosphate fertilizers in order to take advantage of the various nutrients they contain. An agricultural inorganic fertilizer may contain primary, secondary and trace nutrients. Primary nutrients are usually nitrogen (N), phosphorus (P) and potassium (K) while secondary nutrients are calcium, magnesium and sulphur. Trace elements include nutrients such as manganese, zinc, copper and iron. Fertilizers are named only according to the primary nutrients they contain. Those which contain only one or sometimes two primary nutrients retain their chemical name such as superphosphate (P) or ammonium phosphate (N + P). In order to fertilize the pond, the fish farmer needs to pour the fertilizer in a bucket of water and vigorously stir in order to have it fully dissolved. Thereafter, the mixture is poured in the various portions of the pond. The clear pond water eventually turns green after one to two weeks.

Organic fertilizers are especially very essential and effective for small scale fish farmers who are keen to reduce costs. They are a very effective way of increasing natural food supply in ponds to improve fish production. Organic fertilizers come in various forms including animal manures, mostly from farm animals, slaughterhouse wastes, agro-industrial wastes, biogas slurry, cassava fermentation, natural vegetation, compost, and a mixture of various kinds of organic matter (FAO Report, 2005). As pond fertilizers, animal manures have more advantages and should be preferred whenever possible. They provide direct food for the fish and sometimes the fish farmer may not need to buy feed. They are a source of additional carbon dioxide (CO_2), which is very important for the efficient utilization of the nutrients present in the water. This is especially so when used together with inorganic fertilizers. They also increase the abundance of bacteria in the water, which not only accelerate the decomposition of organic matter but also serve as food for the zooplankton, which in turn also increases in abundance. Animal fertilizers also have some disadvantages in that they have low content in primary nutrients (thus tend to be bulky when adding to ponds compared to chemical fertilizers). They have a negative effect on dissolved oxygen content in that they increase the Biochemical Oxygen Demand (BOD) of the pond water needed to break down organic matter for nutrient release. This creates a competition for dissolved oxygen with the fish.

In terms of nutrients, the chemical composition of organic manure varies greatly according to the animal from which it originates - namely the species, age, sex, the nature of its diet. It also depends on the way the manure is handled- namely its relative freshness, conditions of storage and rate of dilution with water. In some cases, total wastes made of dung and urine are available, while in others only solid wastes can be collected. For cattle and pig manure, it is best to use them while they are still fresh. Chicken and duck manures can be used while dry. This is the practice in integrated fish farming. Throughout the world, most of the animal manure is obtained from a limited number of species such as buffalo, cattle (bullock, dairy cows or fattening beef), horses or donkeys, sheep, goats, pigs, rabbits and poultry (chicken, ducks and geese). Chicken droppings are the richest in nutrients. Pig dung is usually richer than sheep or goat dung. Manures from cattle and horses are poorer in nutrients, especially when the animals feed on grass only, their fiber content is relatively high. Buffalo dung is the poorest manure of all.

In terms of use for pond fertilization, you need to put the manure in a sack, tie it firmly and throw it in the pond and leave it between one to two weeks so as to create a greenish coloration in the water. Depending on the pond size, the fish farmer may use two to six 25kg bags of chicken manure for pond fertilization. Alternatively, some fertilizers are poured directly into the pond as illustrated in Fig. 8

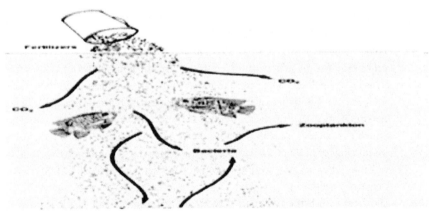

Figure 8: Pond Fertilization. Source: FAO 2003 Report

For pond fertilization with inorganic fertilizers, the farmer needs to use both Urea and Phosphate fertilizers in order to yield better results. The quantities will be 3grams per square meter for Urea while Phosphate will be 2grams per square meter (Trilateral Tilapia Cooperative Project, 2014). This quantification is shown in Table 3 For example, for a 15m x 20m fish pond, the farmer will need 600grams of Phosphate and 900grams of Urea respectively.

When the pond has approx. 20 cm (9 inches) of water you can apply fertilizer. If you use inorganic fertilizer, make sure it is dissolved completely in a bucket before sprinkling it evenly on the water surface. Make sure you splash it into the water and not onto the dykes. When the water becomes green (in 4 to 7 days) you can fill the pond completely up to the desired level. You have to measure the turbidity of the water weekly with a secchi disk or by using your hand. If the disk (or your hand) is not visible at a depth of 30 - 40cm stop fertilizing. Too much fertilizer deteriorates the water quality and oxygen levels.

Table 3. Fertilizer application rates. Source: Trilateral Tilapia Cooperative Project, 2014)

Type of fertilizer	Weekly amount per m^2	Calculation	Weekly amount needed
Di-Ammonium	2g	2g x $300m^2$	600g
Urea	3g	3g x $300m^2$	900g
Dry manure	50g	50g x $300m^2$	15kg

4.4   Check your Progress

In 4.1   we stated that by the end of this chapter, you should be able to:
  (i)   Define pond fertilization;
  (ii)   Explain the requirements for the maintenance of an optimum plankton bloom;
  (iii) Outline the procedure for pond fertilization;
  (iv)   Discuss the advantages and disadvantages of organic fertilizers and animal fertilizers;
  (v)   Recall the application rates for different types of fertilizer;
  (vi)   Correctly fertilize a fish pond.

Now set the booklet aside and test yourself on how many of these outcomes you have achieved.

Chapter Five

UNDERSTANDING WATER SCIENCE

5.1 Learning Outcomes

By the end of this chapter, you should be able to:

(i) Discuss the significance of ensuring optimum water quantity;
(ii) Explain the major aspects of water quality;
(iii) Discuss measures for managing ammonia concentration levels in the fish ponds;
(iv) List the factors which influence dissolved oxygen levels in the fish ponds;
(v) Correctly use water testing instruments.

5.2 Role of water in pond fish farming

Water plays a pivotal role in pond fish farming because it constitutes the enabling environment under which fish thrives. Water is to a fish what a forest is to a baboon. Water is the natural habitat for fish growth and, therefore, should be sufficient in both quantity and quality. Fish performs all their bodily functions of breathing, locomotion, feeding, growth, excretion of waste products, maintaining a healthy salt balance and reproduction in water. Thus, understanding the physical and chemical properties of water is a critical success factor to successful aquaculture.

5.3 Water Quantity

Water quantity requires to be maintained at a depth of 2m all the time so as to allow the fish adequate space for various life activities. Ponds that are 1.5m deep are also within acceptable levels because enough sunlight will be hitting the pond bottom. Low water level is dangerous because it creates a water environment that is full of toxic waste products (fish excreta), nitrates and carbon dioxide that are harmful to the fish. Additionally, the fish will not have sufficient space for movements hence causing fish stress and death. When ponds are deep enough, there will be more water within the pond to dilute toxic waste from the fish. This is one of the reasons for which pond water carrying capacity is an important element in successful fish farming. This, however, depends on the stocking density. Monitoring water quantity must be done daily through a measuring tape or a well-measured and metered stick to ensure the water level is maintained optimally. The biggest challenge with water quantity arises when the fish ponds have leakages. Leakages are known to cause serious farmer stress because fish gets exposed to death by losing their natural habit. Measures must be taken to pump sufficient clean water in the shortest time possible. This explains the need to create a reliable water network for quick supply and replenishment. Some farmers have created big water dams mounted with big pumps capable of pumping large volumes of water to fill ponds in less than an hour. Investment in a water network is always a necessary cost.

5.4   Water Quality

This refers to the chemistry of the water. Water quality is a product of the quality of water at the water source, the quality of the pond soils and immediate environment, production technology and management procedures employed, notably those associated with feeding, the maintenance of adequate dissolved oxygen as well as any other chemicals or inputs applied. Fish requires a live water body in order to survive. Therefore, the chemical composition of the water is of paramount importance. Important factors to consider under water quality are pH, temperature and amount of dissolved oxygen.

5.4.1 *Water pH*

Water pH is a measure of whether water is acidic or basic. Fish have an average blood pH of 7.4, so pond water with a pH close to this is optimum. Studies have demonstrated that fish thrives better in waters whose pH range is 6.5 to 9.0. Water pH can be measured by the pH meters shown in Figure 9

Figure 9 pH Meter   Source: Breathing Fish Farm (2018)

Fish can become stressed in water with a pH ranging from 4.0 to 6.5 and 9.0 to 11.0. Fish growth is limited in water pH less than 6.5, and reproduction ceases and fry can die at pH less than 5.0. Death is almost certain at a pH of less than 4.0 or greater than 11.0. Pond water pH fluctuates throughout the day due to photosynthesis and respiration by plants and vertebrates. Typically, pH is highest at dusk and lowest at dawn. This is because nighttime respiration increases carbon dioxide concentration that interacts with water thereby producing carbonic acid resulting in the lowering of pH. This can limit the ability of fish blood to carry oxygen. Therefore, it is imperative on the fish farmer to constantly maintain the optimum pH range in order to create a conducive environment for fish growth. Generally, pH levels fluctuate between day and night. At night pH levels are more likely to go down as a result of absence of sunlight. Aquatic plants in the fish ponds carry out respiration which uses oxygen and releases carbon dioxide which eventually creates carbonated acids thus reducing the water pH. During the day, the aquatic plants carry out photosynthesis during sunlight hence they use the carbon dioxide and release oxygen. The removal of carbon dioxide reduces the water acidity resulting in more alkalinity. The pH ranges beyond the recommended range have a tendency to stress the fish resulting in loss of locomotion, appetite and death. When the pH levels are staggering below 6.5 the farmer needs to quickly add agricultural lime so as to neutralize the acidity and raise the pH levels. The Rule of thumb requires that the farmer uses 200 grams of agriculture lime ($CaCO^3$) per m^2 dissolved in a bucket of water and sprinkled over the whole fish pond (Trilateral Tilapia Cooperative Project, 2014). However, the first step should be to add more fresh oxygenated water to neutralize the acidity. This method works better if the water source is skewed towards alkalinity. Likewise, when the pH levels in the pond sour beyond 9.0 the farmer needs to urgently add fresh oxygenated water to the pond.

5.4.2 *Water alkalinity*

Alkalinity is water's ability to resist changes in pH and is a measure of the total concentration of bases in pond water including carbonates, bicarbonates, hydroxides, phosphates and borates. These bases react with and neutralize acids, buffering changes in pH. Carbonates and bicarbonates are the most common and important components of alkalinity. In this regard, the farmer needs to add more oxygenated water to the pond. This method should always be taken as the first step. Once again, the pH of the water will be lowered only if the water source is skewed towards acidity. Whenever water is required to neutralize the high pH reading, two proven practices are employed. The farmer will either drain some water at least up to half of the pond and then add more oxygenated water to the pond or the farmer will allow water to drain out through the outlet pipe while simultaneously putting in fresh oxygenated water and allowing this circulation to run for some hours.

Hardness is a measure of alkaline earth elements such as calcium and magnesium in pond water. Hard water has a higher concentration of alkaline earths. Calcium and magnesium are essential to fish for metabolic reactions such as bone and scale formation. Additionally, hardness and total alkalinity can affect pH through interaction with the carbon dioxide cycle. During cold seasons, fish metabolizes food slower and so, it is important that the farmer checks ammonia and nitrate contents in the fish ponds. A rapid increase in ammonia and nitrates in the fish ponds can be toxic for the fish. Ammonia increases in the pond because of fish excreta and decomposed feed which sink to the bottom of the pond during feeding. This emphasizes the importance of strategic feeding where only a little edible feed is thrown into the pond at a time. The quality of the feed also plays a pivotal role. Good feed needs to float on water to allow the fish to eat. When there is decomposed matter at the bottom of the pond, the fish farmer needs to clean the pond bottom in order to maintain the water quality in the fish pond. This significantly helps to maintain ammonia-free ponds or at least reduces it for better fish health. The most tolerable levels of ammonia need to be less than 0.05 mg/l of the toxic form of ammonia (Karki, 2016). The proportion of un-ionised ammonia (NH_3) tends to increase when the pH of water increases above 7.0. When there are high levels of ammonia in the pond, the fish fail to eliminate ammonia from their blood. According to Yuen and Chew (2010), ammonia is excreted by fish as a by-product of protein metabolism primarily through their gills. High concentration of ammonia in water reduces the ability of the gills to do so. The following are some of the measures to manage ammonia concentration levels in the fish ponds:-

Limiting Feeding Rates: Provide only what the fish can consume at each feeding instant. When fish are fed, it is easy to detect overfeeding. This is because the unconsumed feed will accumulate at the pond bottom in the feeding areas. Froth or bubbles, with or without a bad smell, tend to appear on the water surface above the feeding areas when accumulated wasted feed starts decomposing. The pond bottom in the area where fish feed should be the cleanest around the area when feeding. Then, check the pond bottom for signs of excessive buildup of left over feed at least weekly, before you change the ration or when the fish's response declines and you suspect overfeeding. Check the pond bottom for accumulated left-over feed by scooping the mud with your hands to find out whether or not there is excess feed and how much feed there is. You can also check by standing with bare feet in the pond to feel how clean and firm the feeding area is.

Controlling Water pH by preventing it rising above 9: Water that is relatively hard (alkalinity > 60 ppm as $CaCO_3$) has a better buffering capacity against pH fluctuations. If the waters and soils where the ponds are located are either soft (< 60 ppm and/or acidic (pH < 6), lime the ponds with agricultural lime ($CaCO_3$) rather than with builders lime (Ca $(OH)_2$) or quick lime (CaO). This is because agricultural lime is more balanced as a compound as it is made of both a divalent base (CO_3^{2}) and cation (Ca^{2+}) which increase both the alkalinity and hardness of the water. Consequently, it does not cause pH spikes as opposed to builders and quick lime. It also contains carbon (C) as a source of nutrients for phytoplankton (Soma et al., 1999). Increase water exchange through the pond only when the pond gets near its carrying capacity. Water should only be allowed to flow through the pond when the pond's water quality becomes poor due to waste buildup such as when it is approaching carrying capacity. The objective of doing so is to flush out and dilute wastes in the pond as to improve pond water quality. The best way to 'flush' is by reducing the pond water level half way and then refilling it within a half to one day. It is best to drain the water from the bottom when intending to flush. In order to do this, the stand pipe is lowered to the bottom of the pond. Once the water level in the pond has dropped half way, the stand pipe is raised and fresh water is let into the pond to re-fill it. If one cannot flush as recommended due to low water flow on the farm, and low rainfall, then one should not exceed a standing crop of 15 tons/ha. Note that the water leaving the pond is full of nutrients and should be used for crop agricultural.

5.4.3   *Water Temperature*

Water temperature is yet another important element to consider because Tilapia performs better in warm climates. Water temperature is measured by the Fish Pond Thermometer as shown in Figure 10

Figure 10 Fish Pond Thermometer. Source: Breathing Fish Farm (2018)

Temperature ranges of between 20°C and 30°C are favourable for tilapia growth and health. When temperatures go down below 20°C, fish mortality is known to increase. In cold seasons, fish lose appetite, movements and become inactive. During this time, the farmer needs to take steps to safeguard the fish otherwise most of them will die. In this case, the farmer needs to ensure that the pond is filled with water to full capacity. In this way, the bottom water will be warmer than the surface one hence helping the fish escape the extreme weather conditions. Commercial farmers can opt for fish pond heaters to raise the pond temperature to the required set temperature. Extreme care must be taken in order not to harm the fish. Extreme lower winter temperatures are not favourable for fish. This explains why in areas that experience extreme low winter temperatures, fish pond depth is a critical consideration. During lower temperatures, the fish will elect to lie deep in warmer waters at the bottom of the pond. Therefore, if the fish pond is shallow, the fish will freeze to death.

5.4.4   *Dissolved Oxygen (DO)*

Another very important factor is dissolved oxygen. Dissolved oxygen (DO) is a vital indicator of an aquatic ecosystem because it is essential to life – for respiration and other chemical reactions. Low DO levels can affect the creatures that live in a body of water. In fact, an entire aquatic system can "die" if there is insufficient DO in the water, similar to what happens in the process called eutrophication. The amount of dissolved oxygen is measured by the oxygen meter illustrated in Figure 11

Figure 11 Dissolved Oxygen Meter. Source: Perry L, (2011).

Fish rely on dissolved oxygen for their survival in water. Therefore, the more oxygen the water has, the better the fish health and vice versa. If you observe that your fish are gasping for breath on the surface of the water, it means there is less dissolved oxygen and it's time to urgently replenish the oxygen in the fish ponds. The most commonly used traditional method to add oxygen to the fish pond, is to pour fresh water into the pond. In so doing, ensure that the water is falling into the pond from a considerable height. Likewise, the water needs to fall in the form of rain droplets so that it picks more oxygen from the air. This method is reliable and has tremendously helped fish farmers. Oxygen dissolves into water from two sources: from the atmosphere and from plants in the water. The primary source of oxygen for a pond is from microscopic algae (phytoplankton) or submerged plants. In the presence of sunlight, these produce oxygen through photosynthesis and release this oxygen into the pond water. This works better in earthen fish ponds where more aquatic plants perform better (FAO, 2005).

Another proven though costly method of maintaining good supply of oxygen in a fish pond is use of fountains (aeration). This is very important because as water circulates in the deeper parts of the pond, it helps to break down organic compounds thereby providing better quality oxygenated water. Usually, the bottom of the pond has less oxygen compared to the upper pond layers. When you expose the bottom of the pond to oxygen, rich water will have aerobic bacteria breaking down the organics. This will reduce foul odors in the pond, which are caused by anaerobic bacteria action. Harmful gasses can also be released to the atmosphere and oxygen absorbed very easily (FAO, 2006). Anaerobic bacteria work in the absence of oxygen and cause septic conditions in the bottom of the pond. A pond not only needs to absorb oxygen from the air but it also needs to release carbon dioxide and hydrogen sulfide among other gases. Hydrogen sulfide is produced by anaerobic bacteria breaking down organic matter in the bottom of the pond. Under water oxygen pumps can also be used to speedily put oxygen in the fish pond (FAO, 2006).

5.4.5   *Factors that influence Dissolved Oxygen Levels in the fish ponds*

Aquatic life – organisms living in water use up some of the DO for life. Bacteria also use oxygen when decompose organic materials, such as animal waste.

Temperature – cold water holds more DO than warm water. A measurement taken early in the morning when the temperature is lower may be as much as 1mg/l higher than a temperature taken at noon.

Photosynthesis – counteracts the temperature a little as sunlight results in more photosynthesis, which produces oxygen.

Water Turbulence – more turbulence creates increased opportunities for oxygen to enter the water.

Altitude – there is less oxygen in the atmosphere at higher altitude and less DO

Minerals/salinity – distilled water can absorb the most oxygen. The more minerals or salt in the water, the less oxygen the water can hold

Fertilizers/algal blooms – fertilizers lead to an over-production of algae, which limits the sunlight and plant growth in lower levels of water. Dying plants add to the decay resulting in a lower level of photosynthesis and lower oxygen levels

Waste material – fish waste materials and agricultural waste in water can also use up the oxygen in water to support the increasing amounts of bacteria.

5.4.6   *Water Testing Instruments*

In order to ensure better management of the water quality, a fish farmer needs to have various instruments to measure various properties of the water. These instruments include pH Water Testing Kit; Fish Pond Thermometer and Dissolved Oxygen Testing Kit. Some of these instruments come in form of a combination of all the above instruments into one. Dissolved Oxygen (DO) is most often measured using two proven methods:-

Relying on a hand-held meter with a probe using new luminescence technology. This is recommended because no chemicals are required. Secondly, using a hand-held meter with a probe that measures several parameters important for water quality (pH/Redox, Conductivity / TDS and DO / Temperature). The recommended dissolved oxygen levels for fish is between 4mg/l to 11mg/l. Levels souring higher or lower than this range result in fish mortality.

0–2mg/l: DO levels too low to support aquatic life
2–4mg/l: very few fish and aquatic insects can survive
4–7mg/l: good for many aquatic animals, low for cold water fish
7–11mg/l: ideal for most stream fish.

Nevertheless, traditionally a farmer can test water quality by the use of the hand. If a farmer's hand is lowered into the fishpond up to the elbow and yet he is able to see his fingers, then the water quality is good enough for fish survival otherwise the water quality may need further improvement (FAO, 2006).

5.5   Check your progress

In 5.1   we stated that by the end of this chapter, you should be able to:

(i)   Discuss the significance of ensuring optimum water quantity;

(ii)   Explain the major aspects of water quality;

(iii)   Discuss measures for managing ammonia concentration levels in the fish ponds;

(iv)   List the factors which influence dissolved oxygen levels in the fish ponds;

(v)   Correctly use water testing instruments.

Now set the booklet aside and test yourself on how many of these outcomes you have achieved.

Chapter Six

FISH FARMING SEED - FINGERLINGS

6.1   Learning Outcomes

By the end of this chapter, you should be able to:

(i)   Describe the necessary preparations to be made before stocking fingerlings;

(ii)   List the factors which determine fingerling stocking density;

(iii)   Justify the appropriate size of fingerlings to stock;

(iv)   Calculate fingerling stocking density;

(v)   Outline the fingerling stocking process; and

(vi)   Correctly stock fingerings.

6.2   Stocking the fingerlings

After the pond has been fully fertilized, the next step is stocking the pond with fingerlings. Fingerlings constitute fish seed. This book will not delve deep into fingerling production and management because this subject is the preserve of the hatchery. Before fingerlings are acquired, the fish farmer needs to ensure that the correct fish feed (fry mash) is available in adequate quantities. Homemade feed is equally acceptable especially for small-scale farmers who cannot afford commercial feed. However, a well fertilized pond has enough natural feed (phytoplankton) for the fingerlings. The farmer also needs to ensure that the water quality is within the acceptable ranges for fish growth and survival. This will require carrying out measurements of pH, temperature and dissolved oxygen as key parameters. Additionally, the fish farmer needs to ensure that skill is applied when stocking the fingerlings to avoid catastrophes. Immerse the plastic bag container carrying fingerlings into the pond without mixing its content, leave for about 10 minutes for the fish to acclimatize. Open the bags to allow the water from the pond to mix gradually with that in the plastic bag. Thereafter, the fingerlings should be allowed to swim off into the pond on their own. Stocking skills are fairly easy to master and fish farmers can easily carry them out without a challenge. The procedure is illustrated in Figure 12

Figure 12 (a) Fingerlings (b) Stocking fingerlings in a pond. Source: Breathing Fish Farm (2018)

Fry matures into fingerlings after a period of three weeks (21 days) before they are ready for stocking. At this stage, the fingerlings will be weighing about 2-4grams each. Depending on the purpose, farmers will either acquire male fingerlings only (mono culture) or both male and female fingerlings. However, the common practice is acquisition of male fingerlings only so as to ensure uniform fish growth. This helps in calculations of profit margins and in the management of feed. Sex reversal is the process that is used to convert female fingerlings into males using hormones. Recently, scientists at the University of Wales, Swansea, UK have developed a way to produce all male tilapia fish biologically (YY technology) without the use of hormones (Beardmore, Mair & Lewis, 2000). All male tilapia are necessary for maximum production. If females are present in a pond, some of the metabolic energy will be channeled to reproduction limiting those meant for growth of fish. This will also bring about complications of space. The farmer will also have challenges of knowing the correct feed to give the fish because of mixed individual ages. Male fish become sexually mature very quickly and are not worth eating because they fail to grow big enough for business. However, when their maturation is inhibited, the males put their energy into growth and become ready for the market within five to six months. Table 4 shows how to Distinguish good from bad fingerlings.

Table 4 Distinguishing good from bad fingerlings

Issues to Observe	Good fingerlings	Bad Fingerlings
Body Colour	Blackish Green	Grayish Pale
Behaviour(when current is created in the container)	Can swim against current	They gather at the center of container
Food	Stomach is full of food	Stomach is empty

6.3   Number of fingerlings to stock (Stocking Density)

A fish farmer needs to be very careful on the number of fingerlings to stock. This is known as stocking density. Usually the less fingerlings stocked per square meter, the better the health and growth of the fish. Several authors and scholars have given various stocking densities. Fingerling stocking density depends upon purpose of fish farming activity and investment in technical mechanization capabilities. Technical mechanizations capabilities refer to the amount of aeration equipment available to supplement dissolved oxygen in the water. Without proper management, fish growth will be seriously inhibited if your stocking density is too high because the fish will be competing for oxygen resulting in gasping and increased mortality. Oxygen supplementation will be required by use of aeration pumps and paddlewheels. Gianluigi (2013) explains that, tilapia farmers normally rely on river flows and diesel pumps to maintain stable water quality conditions and to renew the dissolved nutrients that sustain healthy algal blooms in their extensive and intensive ponds. This process introduces freshly oxygenated water and helps flush out waste.

Nevertheless, to further increase oxygen levels, some semi-intensive farms and most of the intensive farms use paddlewheels and aspirating aerators, electrical/mechanical devices that add oxygen to the water. They are used at night and early in the morning when oxygen levels are at their lowest. Paddlewheels slap, beat and churn oxygen into the surface of the water; aspirators inject an oxygen-rich stream of water below the surface. Paddlewheel aerators have many moving parts and a lot of down time; aspirators have few moving parts and help to add oxygen at the pond bottom. The above-mentioned systems are normally used in intensive system and are costly.

Oxygen aeration is especially important when the fish have reached 100 grams because at this weight, their oxygen demands have increased. With regard to tilapia stocking density, Negroni (2013) recommends 1 – 4 fingerlings per square meter while Diana, Yi and Lin (2016) recommend three stocking density levels according to investments and managements as follows: Low Stocking Density (LSD) 1-4 fingerlings per square metre, Medium Stocking Density (MSD) of 5-6 fingerlings/m^2 and High Stocking Density (HSD) of 7 – 9 fingerlings/m^2. The above assertions are supported by Shoko, Limbu and Mgaya (2016) who postulate that stocking densities should be 3, 6 and 9 fingerlings per square meters to meet various business requirements amid investment in quality management practices. In summary stocking density depends upon

(i)   availability of water source and volume
(ii)   water management techniques to be adopted
(iii) desired size/volume expected at harvest
(iv) groundwater capacity in earthen pond
(v)   feed type and volume to be used
(vi) estimated mortality rate based on previous experience

The stocking densities are summarized here below:-

Low Stocking Density (LSD)   1 – 4   Fingerlings per Square Meter **[recommended]**

Medium Stocking Density (MSD)   5 – 7   Fingerlings per Square Meter [recommended under good management practices]

High Stocking Density (HSD)   8 – 12 Fingerlings per Square Meter [not recommended but can be tried under extreme professional management practices]

In order to use MSD and HSD, it is highly recommended that the farmer invests in oxygen aeration and frequent water circulation mechanisms. Additionally, the farmer may invest in bio-filtration to breakdown metabolic waste in order to improve the fish living environment. Without these investments, the farmer is strongly advised to employ LSD. However, the rule of the thumb is that the less the stocking density the better the fish health and growth. This calculation is very important because if not well handled, the farmer may either over-stock or under-stock. Overstocking is dangerous because it results in fish overcrowding thus denying the fish of survival space and necessary life nutrients. Usually this leads to stunted fish growth, diseases and high levels of mortality. Under stocking becomes an issue only in terms of business turn over, otherwise it is acceptable. In terms of business, under stocking could result in heavy losses. Now in order for the farmer to calculate the optimum number of fingerlings to stock, he needs to know the area of his pond. This brings to light the importance of pond shape. Rectangular and square shaped ponds are encouraged because it is much easier for the farmer to calculate the fish pond area which then is used in fish pond stocking calculations.

6.4   Size of Fingerlings to Stock

It is highly recommended that the fish farmer stocks fingerlings of the same age and weight. Stocking fingerlings of different sizes creates challenges of feeding because the larger fish may need a higher-level feed while the smaller fish may require a lower level feed. Additionally, when there is little food in the pond, the larger fish may resort to cannibalism. Smaller fish will be eaten up by the larger ones thus reducing the number of fish in the pond. Therefore, farmers need to make sure that they are getting fingerlings of the same size in terms of weight. It is highly recommended that fish farmers get fingerlings which are at least 5grams and above in weight. At this weight, the fingerlings will not stunt but steadily grow because they have overcome challenges of infancy. Nevertheless, most hatcheries in Zambia are selling fingerlings of between 0.5 – 1 gram in weight. This is posing a serious threat because the fish farmer spends much more time and resources to grow these fingerlings and also mortality is high resulting in losses. The stuntedness exhibited is attributed to the longer distances that these fingerlings have to endure to access food in the large water body. In swimming longer distances, the fingerlings lose considerable amounts of energy thus resulting in stuntedness in the initial stages.

6.5   Stocking Density Calculations

For a farmer whose rectangular fish pond measures 30m x 10m, the area would be 300m^2 and using our standard stocking density (at minimum) of 4 fingerlings per square meters, the number of fingerlings required for stocking would be 1,200. For a farmer whose squared shaped fish pond measures 50m x 50m, the area of the pond would be 2500m^2 resulting in 10,000 fingerlings for stocking if we use 4 fingerlings/square meter.

6.6   Fingerling Stocking Process

Fingerlings are usually transported from the hatchery in oxygen-filled plastics to the farm. It is recommended that within 6 hours the fingerlings need to be stocked otherwise they will die of suffocation and stress. Stress comes from the shake-ups as the fingerlings are being transported from the hatchery to the farm. The process of stocking is fairly easy. Upon arrival at the farm, the fish farmer needs to place the oxygen-filled plastics of fingerlings inside the fish ponds for close to 10 minutes without opening the plastics. This is important because it equalizes the temperature of the water inside the plastic to that of the water in the fish pond. Additionally, this helps to make the fingerlings rest a while after a stressful period. Stocking the fingerlings immediately upon arrival usually results in heavy losses because of shock. The fish pond water temperature may not be at the same level as that in the plastics. This, therefore, results in fingerling shock. After the 10 minutes, the fish farmer can open the oxygen-filled plastics and gently fold them up and deep one end in the pond water such that the pond water mixes with that in the plastic. The fingerlings will then start coming out on their own from the plastic into the fish pond. The farmer is advised not to offload the fingerlings into the fish pond as this may shock the fingerlings.

6.7   Check your Progress

In 6.1   we stated that by the end of this chapter, you should be able to:

(i)   Describe the necessary preparations to be made before stocking fingerlings;
(ii)   List the factors which determine fingerling stocking density;
(iii)   Justify the appropriate size of fingerlings to stock;
(iv)   Calculate fingerling stocking density;
(v)   Outline the fingerling stocking process; and
(vi)   Correctly stock fingerings.

Now set the booklet aside and test yourself on how many of these outcomes you have achieved.

Chapter Seven

FISH FEED AND FEEDING PROCESS

7.1 Learning Outcomes

By the end of this chapter, you should be able to:

(i)   Identify types of fish feed;

(ii) Explain feeding rations ad frequencies;

(iii) List the types and order of fish feed;

(iv) Record feeding rates and frequencies;

(v)   Outline the procedure for sample weighing;

(vi) Correctly carry out sample weighing.

7.2 Types of fish feed

Generally, there are predominantly two types of food available to the fish: natural and formulated feed. According to Carballo et al (2008), natural fish food consists of phytoplankton, zooplankton, periphyton, water plants, etc produced in the pond itself while formulated fish feed is produced outside the pond and supplied to the fish regularly to further increase the amount of nutrients in the pond.

Research has shown that the natural fish food largely consists of phytoplankton. The amount of phytoplankton can be increased by the addition of fertilizer to the pond. Formulated feed can either be complete or supplementary. Complete feeds are nutritionally complete (e.g. those sold by commercial feed companies). These are required where natural foods are absent or are a minor source of nutrition. Supplemental feed is feed is that which is nutritionally incomplete. This may be single ingredient (e.g. maize bran) or multi-ingredient such as processed feed. Typical examples of supplementary fish feed are rice bran, broken rice, breadcrumbs, cereals, cereal wastes, maize meal, guinea grass, napier grass, fruits, vegetables, peanut cake, soybean cake and brewer's waste (Carballo et al; 2008). Ha nninen (2014) explains that most Zambian small scale fish farmers rely on fishmeal, peanut meal, soybean meal, rice bran, broken rice, moringa, maize bran and vitamin/mineral premixes to make their own fish formulation.

Owing to the fact that fish feed in Zambia is expensive averaging K300 per 50kg bag of feed, most of the small scale fish farmers have opted to making their own feed. This is viewed as a cheaper alternative. The health and growth of the fish does not depend on whether the feed is commercial or traditionally made but relies on the quality of the feed ingredients and feed itself.

Fish feed is a very important factor for fish health and growth. The quality of feed usually determines the rate of fish growth as well as the taste of the fish. Therefore, fish farmer needs to pay extra attention to the type of feed that he is giving to the fish. Fish grow better when they are given a balanced diet (complete feeds). While farmers may make their own fish feed, it is highly recommended that standard, tested and tried feed be used for better results. The type and order of fish feed is tabulated below in Table 5

Table 5 Feed Types Source: Breathing Fish Farm (2018)

Feed Type	Description
Fry Mash	Feed for one month. Weigh every 2 weeks and when the fish is 15 grams; stop feeding them fry mash and Start crumble. This may take about 1 month.
Crumble	Feed them on crumble…weighing every 2 weeks and when the fish is <u>80 grams</u> then stop crumble and use pre-starter feed.
Pre-Starter	Feed them on pre -starter….weighing every 2 weeks and when the fish is <u>120 grams</u> or between 120g and 150g stop pre-starter and use grower feed.
Grower	Use grower feed until the fish weighs <u>300grams.</u> At this level you may harvest and sell or you may grow them further.
Finisher	Feed the fish until it weighs between 400g – 600g. Harvest and sell

7.3   Feeding Rations and Frequencies

When it comes to feeding rations, there are many schools of thought based on experiences and research. Álvaro (2005) advises that the amount of food that should be fed to the tilapia fish should be based on a percentage of their weight and average size. He further explains that 15 to 20 percent of the fish's body weight should be provided daily for fish of 0.5 grams or less. He adds that 1.5 percent should be fed to fish of 400 grams. As would be expected many fish reside in between these two sizes and their rations can be determined from Table 6. As a comparison to Álvaro's feeding information, Riche and Gargling (2003) claim that small fish should be fed quantities of 10 to 30 percent of their body weight and fish in excess of one-hundred grams should be fed 1.5 percent to 3 percent of their body weight. Again many fish will inevitably reside in between these two sizes. Adding to the arguments on feeding rate, Palabana Fish Research Institute is also within the same values plus minus as can be seen in Table 7

Table 6   Feeding Rate. Source: FAO (2004)

Fish Weight (grams)	Daily Feeding Rate (% Biomass) ..
< 0.5	15-20
0.5	15-20
1	11.0
2	9.0
5	6.5
10	5.2
15	4.6
20	4.2
30	3.6
60	3.0
100	2.5
175	2.5
300	2.1
400	1.5

Table 7 Feeding Rates and Frequencies. Source: FAO (2005)

Feed Type	Average Body Weight (g)	Feeding Rate	Feeding Frequency
Fry Mash	0.5 - 1.5	12%	5x
Fry Mash	1.5 - 5.0	10%	4x
Fry Mash	5.0 – 15	6.5%	4x
Fingerling Meal	15 – 30	6.0%	4x
Fingerling Meal	30 – 80	5.0%	3x
Juvenile	80 – 120	4.0%	3x
Juvenile	120 – 200	3.0%	3x
Juvenile	200 – 300	2.5%	3x
Juvenile/green pond	300 upwards	2.0%	2x

Table 7 indicates the fact that the farmer needs to carefully calculate the daily feed ration so that he/she does not overfeed or underfeed the fish. The daily ration is the amount of feed required to feed the fish per day and this is dependent on the body weight of the fish. When the daily feed ration is calculated, it must then be divided by the number of feeding times so as to know the quantity of feed to give the fish at each specific time of the day. The farmer therefore, needs to have a scale to carefully weigh the calculated feed ration. From experience feeding is recommended to be done around the pond and not throwing the feed in one place. This is because fish has a tendency to injure each other as they jostle for the feed, this causes diseases and mortality. Feeding timings need to be strictly adhered to because fish has a tendency to master the feeding times. Usually, when it is feeding time, fish will normally linger in the feeding areas waiting for the feed. This is a conditioned reflex action. During feeding, it is highly recommended that only little feed be thrown into the fish pond at a time. This helps to prevent wastage of feed and preserves water quality. Throwing in too much feed at a time is dangerous because most of the feed will sink at the bottom of the pond resulting in decomposing debri that will eventually produce ammonia thereby contaminating the water. In terms of the number of days to feed the fish, it is recommended that the fish are fed only six (06) days in a week to allow them a day of rest and reliance on aquatic organisms in the water.

Question

A fish farmer has 4,000 fingerlings in his pond and has observed that his fish are weighing 12.2g after 1 month 2 weeks. Calculate the daily feed ration and the amount of feed at each feed instance assuming that he feeds them 4 times per day. Use 6.5% as percent of body weight.

Solution

6.5%/100% x 12.2g = 0.793grams. This represents the daily feed ration for one fingerling. Now since the number of fingerlings is 4,000; we have 0.793grams x 4,000 and we get 3,172grams (3.2kg). This, then, becomes the feed ration (amount of feed to give the fish per day).

Now arising from the fact that the farmer is feeding his fish 4 times per day, we divide this quantity by 4. Thus, 3,172grams/4 = 793grams. This is the amount of feed that the farmer will actually give the fish at each feeding interval. This calculation is very important because it ensures that the fish are neither underfed nor overfed. Daily feed ration needs to be carefully calculated every two (2) weeks to determine the correct amounts of feed to give the fish for better and healthier growth.

7.4   Sample Weighing

Usually fish is weighed every two (2) weeks to determine its growth levels. This is called sample weighing or fish sampling. Fish is caught using a cast net which is thrust or thrown into the fish pond and pulled out with a sampled quantity of fish. This fish is then weighed on a digital scale (if the fish are still small) and then the total weight is divided by the number of the fish weighed. This gives a representative Average Body Weight (ABW) of the fish. The ABW helps to monitor fish growth and also determines whether feed and feed quantities can be changed or not. An example of a cast net is presented in Figure 13.

Half Mesh Size
3/8 inch (Thickness:0.3mm)

Figure 13 Cast Net   Source: Amazon.com (2018)

Usually increasing fish appetite is one of the farmer's important preoccupation because it helps in the healthy growth of the fish. Research has shown that adding salt to the fish feed results in increased appetite for the fish by increasing feed palatability. The salt is not added to the pond but it is part of the feed in the range of 0.5 to 1% (Mzengereza and Kang'ombe, 2016). Furthermore, Coche *et al.* (2013) have demonstrated that light has a motivational effect on fish appetite. The study reports specifically that red light motivates and stimulates the fish to eat. Nevertheless, fish appetite can be increased when the general water quality conditions are good and suitable for fish growth and the feed quality is of a high standard. According to Gianluigi (2013), the average growth of Tilapia *niloticus* is between 0.8 to 1.2grams per day in a good farming condition for a mixed sex population reared at a suitable temperature. Better growth performance is achieved when 100% male populations are used as the stock and also when improved genetic strains are reared. In these extremely good situations, some fish farmers can obtain growth of **4 grams per day**, for fish >350 g.

7.5 Check your progress

In 7.1 we stated that by the end of this chapter, you should be able to:

(i)   Identify types of fish feed;
(ii)   Explain feeding rations ad frequencies;
(iii)   List the types and order of fish feed;
(iv)   Record feeding rates and frequencies;
(v)   Outline the procedure for sample weighing;
(vi)   Correctly carry out sample weighing.

Now set the booklet aside and test yourself on how many of these outcomes you have achieved.

Chapter Eight

FISH POND MANAGEMENT

8.1   Learning Outcomes

By the end of this chapter, you should be able to:

(i)   Explain the importance of effective pond management;

(ii)   Discuss the major aspects of effective pond management;

(iii)   Identify both behavioral and physical signs of fish ill health;

(iv)   Explain the process of water quantity management;

(i)   Effectively manage water quantity;

(ii)   Outline the process of monitoring fish behavior; and

(iii)   Effectively monitor fish behavior.

8.2   Effective Pond Management

Perhaps the most important of all activities is fish pond management. Many farmers make fatal mistakes by concentrating only on the pre-stocking activities and abandoning the pond after the fish has been introduced to the pond. Daily pond management determines success or failure of the fish farming activity. There are several factors that the fish farmer needs to consider in order to produce healthy fish.

8.2.1   Fish Appetite

Monitoring fish behavior is of great importance because it provides some insights of fish health. If fish appears to have lost appetite, it is a sign that something is wrong. It could be because temperatures have fallen too low (below 20°C). Temperature plays an important role in stimulating fish appetite. Fish health and appetite are motivated by optimum temperatures of between 20°C and 30°C. This explains why successful fish farming must be practiced in warm environments and climates. However, tilapia fish can still be cultured in temperate climates under controlled temperature environments using fish pond heaters. Decreased fish appetite may also be a sign of poor water quality. The fish farmer may need to check the water transparency and pH levels. When pH levels rise beyond the recommended levels, fish get stressed and consequently lose appetite. The recommended pH levels for better fish growth must between 6.5 and 9.0. Fish may also lose appetite if they are being fed with wrong feed. It is important for the farmer to provide the correct feed for the size of the fish. Providing grower feed to fingerlings may become a deadly snare as they will not eat because the feed is meant for full-grown fish and the smaller baby fish may not manage to eat. Also, farmers need to be careful with the quality of fish feeds given to the fish because if the quality is poor, the fish may shun the feed. This happens especially when the farmer is making his own feed. It is extremely important to ensure accuracy with regard to combination ratio and appropriateness with regard to ingredients in order to meet fish requirements. When a fish farmer observes poor appetite for the fish, it is a sign that the fish are stressed because of the environment. In this situation, the farmer is advised to stop feeding the fish. He/she then needs to carry out sample weighing so as to establish the average body weight of the fish. This will help to determine the best-feed type for the fish based on the weight. Additionally, the farmer needs to test and improve the water quality conditions so that the fish have a suitable environment for healthy growth. After this, the farmer needs to weigh the correct amount of feed to give the fish.

8.2.2   *Fish Gasping and Oxygenation*

If the farmer observes that the fish are gasping for breath, it is a vital sign that oxygen levels are low in the pond. The longer it stays like this, the more the likelihood of increased fish mortality, the farmer needs to stop feeding the fish. Throwing feed in the pond will be a waste of feed because the fish will not manage to eat. They are severely stressed and their survival is on the line. The farmer will need to pour in fresh water that should be falling at some height. The idea here is that the fresh water gathers oxygen in the air before it lands into pond water. Additionally, the falling water must be made into a spread spectrum or rain droplets so that more oxygen is gathered. This is the most common method that many fish farmers use to boost oxygen levels in the pond. When this is happening, you will observe that all the fish will be gathered around the area where the fresh water is falling. This is because there is enough oxygen there and life conditions are favorable. This method is for farmers with boreholes. However, farmers with fish ponds near rivers and streams may simply divert the water into their ponds. In this way, the water gathers more oxygen as it traverses through the furrow from the river into the pond. River and stream water has a lot of dissolved oxygen which borehole water does not have. Additionally, the farmer may resort to aeration. Here the farmer may introduce a pump that throws pond water up and down and in so doing the water is gathering oxygen. This method is highly effective when the amount of water being thrown up is large enough.

8.2.3   *Salinization*

Salinization is the process of salting the fish so as to prevent and kill pathogens. Sometimes, fish catches pathogens and diseases. If you suspect that the fish in your pond has been exposed to infection, the best remedy is to cull the fish and put it in salinized pond water in a container for close to 5 minutes after which the fish is introduced back into the pond. Salinizing the fish using non-iodized salt helps to destroy the pathogens and preserve the tilapia fish. It should also be mentioned that, if you are raising your tilapia in water that already contains salt, and you get a parasitic outbreak, you can put your tilapia in fresh water to kill the parasites. In a nutshell, parasites cannot handle sudden changes in salinity.

According to Carballo et al (2008), the following are some of the fish disease behavioral signs. These signs basically notify the farmer whether or not the fish is unwell. In situations like these, the fish farmer is advised to call a Veterinary Doctor or a Fish Expert for technical support.

Behavioral Signs of Disease among the fish

Watch out for any of the following:

(i)   Scraping or "Flashing" at the bottom of the pond
(ii)   Fins held still, "clamped" against body
(iii)   Complete loss of appetite ; not eating at all
(iv)   Piling up in a heap at the bottom of the pond or clumped touching each other in a corner

Physical Appearance Signs

Watch out for any of the following:

(i)   Frayed or missing fins normally caused by trauma from overcrowding;
(ii)   One or more variable sized red sores usually caused by bacterial infection;

(iii)   Many tiny white spots on the skin;

(iv)   Shallow non-bloody ulcers on the skin;

(v)   Skin moves or "shimmers" when held out of water; and

(vi)   Raised white to pinkish patches on the skin;

(vii)   Lumps growing on surface of skin;

(viii)   Cloudy eyes;

(ix)   One eye popping (physical trauma and infection, or cancer in or behind the eye); and

(x)   Both eyes popping (gas bubble disease, or caudal kidney infection).

8.2.4   *Water Quantity Management*

Water is required in adequate quantities in order to manage a fish pond. Pond water quantity requires strategic management in order to sustain the fish. Periodically, water requires to be drained and fresh oxygenated water filled-in in order to maintain water quality and quantity. The farmer therefore needs to periodically observe and measure water height (depth). If the water levels in the pond seem to be going down, it is a sign that the pond has some leakages. Leakages are a very serious danger and the farmer must seal them quickly because they can lead to a catastrophe of gigantic proportions. If pond water seeps into the soil overnight, then the fish is definitely going to die. This is a disaster. Pond leakages under the water require special water adhesive to mend when identified. If this adhesive is not available, then the farmer may rely on the traditional method of putting enough wet soil on those identified holes (openings) and then placing a heavy rock on top. This method has been used extensively by many farmers. Nevertheless, if the fish are still small, the farmer can drain all the pond water and put the fish in large dishes or vessels with the existing pond water. Thereafter, the pond plastics (dam liners) can be checked and mended after which more fresh water is filled into the pond again and the fish reintroduced in the pond. Water quantity management is a stressful exercise if not well planned. The farmer needs to have heavy water pumps which can fill the fish pond in a matter of hours to preserve fish life in times of water seepages. Water quantity management is not easy because it requires a robust and sustainable water network that involves water pumps conjoined with poly pipes for water transportation to the ponds. This is because, as feeding is taking place and as life activities are going on in the pond, water quality deteriorates necessitating replacement. As earlier alluded to, water quality is measured by observing the pH of the water. The recommended pH range for fish survival is between 6.5 and 9.0.

8.2.5 *Recirculating the Water*

Sometimes in order to rid the bottom of the fish pond of decaying feed and debris, it is important to circulate the pond water. Too much accumulation of debris at the bottom of the pond is dangerous because it results in release of ammonia that might suffocate and stress the fish. Recirculation is done by opening the outlet pipes for water to flow out of the pond while fresh water is allowed to enter the pond. Care must be taken when opening the outlet pipes because fish may be drained with the water. A sieve needs to be placed tight at the entrance side of the outlet pipe so as to prevent fish flowing together with the water. As contaminated water is flowing out, fresh oxygenated water is pouring into the pond thus creating a circulation in the pond. This circulation will clean the pond bottom. Additionally, budget allowing, specialized equipment is available that is capable of sucking dirt and debris at the pond bottom so as to clean the fish pond. Usually after circulating the water for 4 to 6hrs, the water becomes much more clear and transparent. This breathes new life in the pond for good fish health.

8.2.6 *Floating Substances*

Care must be taken not to allow leaves, grass, plastics and other substances to float on top of the fish pond. These have the tendency of blocking sunlight that is required by aquatic plants like algae for photosynthesis. This process is necessary because it helps in the production of dissolved oxygen that is needed by the fish for survival. The fish farmer, therefore, needs to have a scooping net tied to a long frame to remove all floating materials from the fish ponds. The pond surface requires to be clear and clean all the time. Additionally, grass that is growing on the dykes (banks) needs to be cut so as to avoid breeding grounds for snakes. In fact, special carpet grass can be planted on the dykes in order to hold the soil. Holding the soil is important because it prevents the pond banks from breaking and destroying the ponds.

8.3.7 *Predator Management*

Fish predators are another aspect that the fish farmer needs to manage. Fish predators include, but are not limited to, snakes, birds and water rats. Measures need to be taken to prevent these from attacking and eating the fish.

Birds and water rats are known to be the biggest nuisance with regard to fish predation. Specialized fish pond bird nets are usually hung around the pond to prevent all types of predators especially birds. These fish pond nets are expensive and therefore some farmers resort to clearing and cleaning the pond area so as not to allow grass and shrub growth. Additionally, some farmers rely on tying flying plastics on to sticks (poles) which are then erected around the ponds to scare predator birds. Chemicals can also be sprayed around the ponds to scare away snakes and frogs. Fencing the fish ponds is also a very important aspect of security especially against small children and animals. The pond area is strictly out of bounds for children because they may fall and drown in the ponds. Thus, fencing is an important aspect of securing the ponds. Advanced Commercial Farmers are advised to put surveillance systems like CCTV to monitor activities around the fish ponds.

8.2.8 *Monitoring Fish Behavior*

The farmer needs to be very strategic to succinctly monitor fish behavior for discomforting signs. Usually, when they are healthy, the fish have sufficient energy to swim swiftly especially during feeding times. This behavior is also observed when visitors are lingering around the fish pond area. When the fish are seemingly crowded in one location and unconcerned about intruders, it is an indication that they may be stressed due to sickness or poor quality of water. Fish hanging on the surface, and seemingly gasping for breath, implies that dissolved oxygen levels are low and more oxygen is urgently required in the pond. If the fish are usually found on top of the water most of the time, it implies that they are being underfed and need more food. In this case, the fish farmer needs to carry out sample weighing to determine the feed type and quantities required by the fish.

8.2.9 *Accelerating Fish Growth*

In order to accelerate fish growth, the fish farmer needs to have lower stocking densities or higher stocking densities but with very excellent pond management capabilities and investments. Water quality and quantity needs to be managed in a professional manner so that fish pond environment is conducive for fish growth. Fish feed needs to be of high quality in order for the fish to have a healthier diet for better growth. The farmer needs to stick to the required quantities of feed rations and feeding frequencies. Oxygen supplementation has also proved to be crucial for better fish growth. Fish in very large ponds may not grow at the same level because some of it may not be able to swim early enough to reach the feeding points owing to pond size. The stronger fish will then grow faster than the weaker ones resulting in uneven growth. This, therefore, underscores the need for fish farmers to spread the feed around the pond and not to heap it at one spot.

8.3   Check your Progress

In 8.1 we stated that by the end of this chapter, you should be able to:

(i)   Explain the importance of effective pond management;

(ii)   Identify both behavioral and physical signs of fish ill health;

(iii)   Discuss the major aspects of effective pond management;

(iv)   Explain the process of water quantity management;

(v)   Effectively manage water quantity;

(vi)   Outline the process of monitoring fish behavior; and

(vii)   Effectively monitor fish behavior.

Now set the booklet aside and test yourself on how many of these outcomes you have achieved.

—————— **Chapter Nine** ——————

HARVESTING AND RECORD KEEPING

9.1 Learning Outcomes

By the end of this chapter, you should be able to:

(i)   Explain the procedure for fish harvesting;
(ii)   Distinguish between partial harvesting and full harvesting of fish;
(iii) Correctly harvest fish;
(iv)   List the major components of record keeping; and
(v)   Keep accurate records.

9.2 Harvesting

Harvest is defined as the removal of harvest-sized fish or removal of fish from any stage of the production cycle (Timmons et al., 2001). Normally harvest is credited as one of the most exciting events in a fish farmer's life. The scene of seeing fish harvested makes a fish farmer's heart glow with extreme joy. However, before harvesting can be achieved, a fish farmer needs to adequately prepare. Part of the preparation requires ensuring that a ready market is secured for the fish. This will help the farmer to sell the fish without delay so that the cycle can begin all over again. If the farmer delays to find market, there is usually some panic, which may result in the farmer selling the fish unprofitably. As part of the harvest preparation, the farmer must ensure that fish-harvesting gear is readily available. This gear includes seine (drag) net, bins, baskets, sucks, scales, knives, large cooling containers and a refrigerated truck. Additionally, the farmer needs to slowly reduce the water levels a day before harvesting in order to make the exercise a little easier especially where the pond is very deep. Two days before harvesting, the fish must not be fed and no pond fertilization must take place to prevent strange flavors (feed smell). This allows the fish to purge and remove the bad flavors associated with the feed. Fresh water needs to be pumped in for improved fish quality. Fish should be checked for off flavors. A seine net, also called a drag net, is used for harvesting especially in large fish ponds. It is usually rectangular, with a cork or plastic float line along the top. The bottom of the net is weighted down by lead weights or a chain, and is called the lead line or weighted end. The cork and lead lines extend past the length of the net and these are used to haul the net through the water. The fish harvesting procedure is illustrated in Figure 14.

Figure 14: Seine net. Source: Wikipedia (2018).

Some seine nets are specially designed in such a way that they have a porch or curve in the center portion of the net. Fish normally collect in this area as the net is hauled through the water. A scooping net is also employed to scoop the fish inside the seine net for onward offloading into buckets and big basins. Farmers are advised to use seine nets that are wider than the width of the pond so that fish cannot escape by swimming around it. Seine nets are usually used for complete pond harvesting. Additionally the farmer must make sure that the lead line of the net is at the bottom of the pond to stop fish from escaping under it. Seine nets require at least two people to operate them, with one person guiding each end of the net. More people may be required if larger volumes of fish need to be caught, this is true in big fish ponds.

With regard to actual harvesting, the farmer needs to be clear whether he is going to have partial or full harvesting of the fish. Partial harvesting is where only a few fish are harvested for the customer while full harvesting is where the entire fish pond is emptied of the fish. Extreme care must be taken when it comes to partial harvesting because a lot of fish get stressed and injured in the process resulting in serious post-harvest losses. After a partial harvest, the farmer needs to quickly pump fresh water so as to provide a conducive environment for the remaining fish to thrive. Generally, harvesting needs to be carried out early in the morning or late in the evening when the temperatures are still low to ensure that the harvested fish remains fresh. During harvesting, the farmer is required to cast the seine net at the deeper end of the pond and dragging it towards the shallower end of the pond. Once the net is pulled outside the pond, sort out the fish immediately so that the smaller fish are quickly thrown back into the pond for continued growth while the larger fish are put in buckets. Partial harvesting is normally done by using a gill net tied across the fish pond. Larger fish are caught by their gills as they try to swim across the pond while smaller growing fish slip through the eyes of the net. Seine nets can also be used for partial harvesting with some precautions. In this case, the fish farmer needs to select a particular angle where the seine net will be dragged to catch only the required number of fish needed at that time. This is important to avoid over-stressing the fish.

Depending on the purpose, the fish farmer needs to preserve the harvested fish from bacterial attacks. Getu et al. (2015) assert that fish usually gets spoiled within 12 hours of harvesting due to high temperatures. Now, in order to prevent spoilage of the fish, the bacteria around the fish need to be killed or prevented from growing. Methods to carry out this exercise include smoking, salting, drying, canning as well as cooling and freezing. Most of these preservative methods are inexpensive and the farmer requires just a bit of his time and labor especially in the case where the fish are in large quantities.

9.3   Record Keeping and Costing

A fish farmer needs to carefully manage his/her records so that he/she can ascertain whether profits are being made or not. Each fish pond needs to have its own book of records. Record keeping is the art of documenting all activities around the fish pond ecosystem. This includes recording stocking levels, feed rations, feeding frequencies, number of bags of feed bought, quantities of fertilizers applied per pond, average body weight of the fish per pond, fish mortality per pond, dates of changing types of feed and many more. Record keeping may also include documenting visitations by predators including dates of their visitations and what transpired. Record keeping usually provides the farmer with accurate information necessary for decision-making processes and also for knowledge of fish health and growth. The farmer may intervene if the fish are not growing as expected. Additionally, the farmer will be able to know how much he/she has spent on feed and other requirements so as to ably calculate the profit margins. For clarity on record keeping, kindly see Appendices.

9.4   Check your Progress

In 9.1 we stated that by the end of this chapter, you should be able to:

(i)   Explain the procedure for fish harvesting;
(ii)   Distinguish between partial harvesting and full harvesting of fish;
(iii)   Correctly harvest fish;
(iv)   List the major components of record keeping; and
(v)   Keep accurate records.

Now set the booklet aside and test yourself on how many of these outcomes you have achieved.

PRACTICAL GUIDELINES
FISH POND FARMING

[A]   Pond Siting

Regarding pond siting, proceed as follows:

(i)   Advisably check for flat land;

(ii)   Check for a place without huge underground rocks because excavation becomes difficult;

(iii)   Check for a place near a water source (ever running stream, river or rich water borehole of at least 3 liters per second borehole yield). Will the source of water be enough to last the entire culturing period? Is the water suitable for livestock and human beings? Suitable water for fish farming must not contain excessive dissolved and suspended solids or toxic substances;

(iv)   In case you use a borehole, then check the water table from topographical maps from the Department of Water Affairs so that you are sure of sustainable water availability. Fish need a lot of water.

(v)   Is the water clean, is the quality suitable and pathogen free?

(vi)   Water quality refers to consideration for salinity, temperature, dissolved oxygen, acidity/alkalinity (pH), suspended particulate matter.

(vii)   Test water source for pH [6.5 to 9.0 is ideal].

(viii) Check soil type (clay soil is suitable otherwise pond liners will be required)

(ix)   Avoid sitting a pond in a place that floods because the pond maybe flooded with water and sweep the fish away. Care and investment must be made for this exercise.

(x)   The pond should be in full sunlight and not surrounded by trees as this invites predators, such as fish-eating birds. Sunlight also helps in photosynthesis of algae and phytoplankton thus putting dissolved oxygen in the pond.

(xi)   Avoid siting a pond on a sloppy ground because it may cost more to construct. However, a 5% slope is acceptable.

(xii)   Site the pond near a residential area (for easy pond management and security).

(xiii) Site the pond near a road network for easy transportation of the fish.

(xiv) Consider sustainable availability of power.

[B]   Pond Construction

Regarding pond siting, proceed as follows:

In order to dig a fish pond, you need a number of tools among which are tape measure, rope, spirit measure, hammer, square, 1m long pegs, pick-axe, shovels, wheelbarrows, lime etc. **The following steps will help guide in the process**

1.   Select a suitable site depending on various factors which may include land topology, wind direction, soil type and formation, slope of the land, availability of water etc

2.   Decide on the size of the pond (50 x 25; 40 x 20; 30 x 10 etc) you want to dig depending on factors like available land for fish ponds, water quantity and available budget.

3.   Calculate the apartments of the Pond such that the shallow and Middle sides should be 30% of the length of the pond each while the deeper side is 40% of pond length

4.   Clear the land of any trees, shrubs, grass and bushes

5.   Mark out or stake the land by use of a tape measure while fixing the 1m pegs on the four corners by use of a hammer

6.   Measure the right angles accurately by use of a square and level the pond horizontally and vertically by a spirit measure

7.   Tie all the 1m long pegs on the corners of the pond with a rope or string to show the size of the pond

8.   Measure the pond diagonals to make sure the pond is a perfect rectangle. You can also construct square ponds for easy calculation of pond area. Other shapes are also possible but pose a threat of not calculating the pond area correctly.

9.   Determine the deeper and shallow sides of the pond by relying on the slope of the land and wind direction. Mark the sizes of the shallow, middle and deeper sides according to point no.3 above. Fix the pegs accordingly.

10. From the deeper side of the pond on both ends, mark out a 2.5m while on the shallow side on both ends mark out a 1.0m This will create an outer box representing the dyke slopes. The Water level will be 2.0m on the deeper side while the 0.5m is freeboard (space without water). On the shallow end, 0.5m will be water depth while the other 0.5m is freeboard. This creates the necessary slope required for water to easily flow in the pond. Mark out another third box 1m around the entire pond. This provides the dyke.

11. Digging should start from the shallow side to the deeper side. In so doing, divide the shallow side into smaller boxes that are assigned to people to dig in a day. After the shallow side has been dug, divide the middle and continue until you complete the deeper side in similar fashion.

12. After the pond has been dug, verify the measurements of the dyke slopes on the deeper side (2.5m); shallow side (1.0m) as well as the pond depth from the shallow end to the deeper end of the pond.

13. Level the inside of the pond to create a suitable slope.

14. Construct the water inlet and drainage systems on the shallow and deeper side of the pond respectively with all their accompanying sub-systems. A furrow carefully dug (allowing good slope) from a natural water body to the shallow end of the pond can aid as a water inlet system in the case where source water is from a natural water body while in a case where source water is drawn from a borehole, we could use a polypipe hanging on top of the pond for aeration purposes as an inlet system. The outlet system can be constructed using a 6m 4 inches sewer and elbow on the deeper end.

[C]   **Pond Liners**

Determining Size of Pond Liner Required

According to Celeste et al. (2014), the formula for calculating the correct length for a pond liner is: length + twice the depth + 0.6m. Likewise the pond width will be width + twice the depth + 0.6m. Doubling the depth accounts for lining the two walls and the 0.6m allows an overlap of 0.3m at each end. Therefore, if the fish pond measures 50m long by 25m wide with a depth of 2m, the pond liner size needed would then be 54.6m x 29.6m.

Pond Liner Joining

Requirements: (a) Pond Liner Welder (b) Pond Liner Sealer (c) Tuff Stuff.
In order to join pond liners, proceed as follows:

(i)   Calculate and Measure the correct sizes of pond liners you want to join. Remember the formula above.

(ii)   Let the edges of the pond liners be straight.

(iii) Let the pond liners be of the same thickness e.g 500 microns

(iv)   Let the pond liner welder be placed between the two pieces you intend to join.

(v)   Switch it on and let the pond liner welder move as it joins the pond liners together. Be careful when increasing speed to avoid burning the pond liner through excessive heat.

Pond Liner Sealing

In order to seal pond liners, proceed as follows:

(i)   Sealing normally comes when pond liners have small holes, cracks, breakages or openings. These holes need to be sealed in order to prevent water seepage.

(ii)   Here you use the Pond Liner Sealer (pond liner hot-air gun).

(iii) You need clean good size pond liner patches enough to cover the hole.

(iv)   Put the patch on the hole and then seal using pond liner sealer beginning on the edges while using a soaked mutton cloth for cooling purposes

[D]   Filling Pond With Water

Before filling the pond with water, apply a thin layer of agricultural lime to the bottom of the pond. This will help to eliminate pests like leeches and bacteria that may affect the fish. Thereafter,

(i)   Fill the pond with suitable water. Do not use chlorinated tap water because it is poisonous to fish. Chlorine kills fish.

Suitable water for fish farming can be sourced from underground water and surface water (rivers, streams or lakes etc).

(ii) Ensure the pond is completely filled with water and mark the level of the water and observe for 1 to 2 days to see the rate of water seepage. Seal all the holes (if any) using under water adhesive. You may also traditionally put sufficient wet soil on the portion where water is seeping with a stone on top. After this, you can continue observing until you are sure there is no water seepage anymore. This must be done before stocking. This sorts out water seepage on the pond bottom.

(iii) After being satisfied that seepage is not occurring on the pond bottom, fill the pond completely full and mark the water level. Observe again for a day or two. This test helps to identify seepage on the sides of the pond. If seepage is occurring on the sides, you may use some cement in the case of an earthen pond and pond liner gun in the case of a lined pond.

[E]   Fingerlings

A fingerling seed is a tiny, newly hatched fish weighing between 0.5 and 1 gram. Buy fingerlings which are at least 5grams or higher in weight because these have better resilience and survival rate. Bigger fingerlings are, however, difficult to find and may be expensive at times. Purchase tilapia fingerlings from an established hatchery with good reputation. The fingerlings are normally in plastic bags of fresh water loaded with oxygen. Move the fingerlings to your fish farm as soon as you can to avoid subjecting the fingerlings to severe stress possibly within 6 hours while oxygen last. In Zambia, quality fingerlings can be obtained from First Hatch, Horizon Hatchery, Palabana Fisheries, Msekese Fisheries, Kariba, Chirundu Bream etc.

Number of Fingerlings to Stock

Low Stocking Density (LSD)   1 – 4   Fingerlings per Square Meter
                                    [recommended]

Medium Stocking Density (MSD)   5 – 7   Fingerlings per Square Meter
                                    [recommended under good management practices]

High Stocking Density (HSD)   8 – 12 Fingerlings per Square Meter
[not recommended but can be tried under extreme professional management practices]

For MSD and HSD, the fish farmer requires to heavily invest in better pond management practices which may include oxygen aerators, and proper management of water quality and quantity. Overstocking a pond is dangerous because it results in stunted growth which becomes a drain on fish feed and might result in numerous diseases and poor growth.

Question: Mrs. Tembo has a fish pond behind her home measuring 30m x 20m which is stocked with 1,200 fingerlings. Advise whether the pond is under-stocked or over-stocked? What are the disadvantages of overstocking a pond? Note: Calculate on the basis of 5 Fingerlings/m^2

[F]   Fingerling Stocking

Fingerlings can be stocked from any point of the fish pond. i.e. deeper side, middle or the shallow side. Now, immediately the fingerlings arrive at the farm from the hatchery, you are required to follow the steps below:-

(i)   **Firstly,** lift the heavy plastic bags containing the fingerlings and lower them into the fish pond. Do not untie them at this point but rather leave them as they are for about 10 minutes. The reason is that if you untie and stock them immediately, some fingerlings might die from shock which will be caused by the differences in temperature between the water in the plastic containing fingerlings and the water in the fish pond. The 10 minutes is to allow the temperature in the two environments to be the same.

(ii)   **Secondly,** after the 10 minutes have elapsed, untie the plastic bag containing the fingerlings and fold it up to water level.

(iii) **Thirdly,** deep one side of the plastic bag containing the fingerlings into the pond water such that the pond water gets in contact with the water in the plastic bag. At this point, the fingerlings will start swimming on their own from the plastic bag into the pond while you tilt the plastic bag slightly to assist those that may be hesitant to leave the plastic bag. Do not offload the fingerlings into the pond but let them move on their own from the plastic bag into the pond.

(iv)   After stocking, if you did this somewhere in the middle of the pond, you are required to briefly stand still for about 10 minutes. This is important because during transportation, some fingerlings lost energy as a result of the shaking action of the water. These fingerlings usually sink at the bottom around your legs to recuperate before they can start moving about in the pond. Therefore, if you start moving about immediately after stocking, you risk stepping on these fingerlings around your legs. This action may kill them since they are still weak.

[G]   Testing pH of the Pond Water

pH stands for hydrogen potential. This is basically a scale that measures the neutrality, acidity or alkalinity of the pond water. Fish have an average blood pH of 7.4, so pond water with a pH close to this is optimum. The ideal pH range for optimal fish survival is 6.5 to 9.0 Fish can become stressed in water with a pH ranging from 4.0 to 6.5 and 9.0 to 11.0.

Therefore, in order to test for pH, you need to use the pH Meter. The steps below need to be followed:-

(i)   using a bucket scoop water from the fish pond whose water you want to test;

(ii)   lower the pH meter into the bucket of water up to the water mark level indicated on the pH meter and switch on the meter. For better results, switch on the pH meter while it is dipped into the water; and

(iii) shake the pH Meter for better meter sensor sensitivity and take the reading on the meter. You can repeat this two more times at different points of the pond. Then you can record the average pH readings.

N.B. You can also directly dip the pH meter into the fish pond up to the water mark level, shake it and take the readings

[H]   Testing Pond Temperature

Temperature is an important aspect in fish farming because it aids fish appetite and improves growth. The ideal temperature range for optimal fish survival is 20 degrees Celsius to 30 degrees Celsius. Ideal Temperature Range for tilapia fish is 20°C to 30°C. Best temperature is 25°C. In temperatures below 20°C the fish will not grow steadily. Growth is seriously inhibited. The best time for fish pond farming in Zambia is between August and April. Therefore, in order to test for pond temperature, you need to use a fish pond thermometer. The steps below need to be followed:-

(i)   using a bucket scoop water from the fish pond whose water you want to test;

(ii)   lower the pond thermometer into the bucket of water and leave it for 10 minutes; and

(iii)   The fishpond thermometer screen in your hand will then show the temperature reading.

You can repeat this two more times at different points of the pond. Then you can record the average the average temperature readings.

[I]   Testing Dissolved Oxygen

Dissolved Oxygen (DO) is very important for fish growth. The ideal dissolved oxygen range for optimal fish survival is 4mg/l to 11mg/l. Therefore, in order to test for DO, you need to use the DO meter. The steps below need to be followed:-

(i)   using a bucket, scoop water from the fishpond whose water you want to test;

(ii)   Lower the DO meter into the bucket of water up to the water mark level indicated on the DO meter. For better results, switch on the DO meter while it is dipped into the water; and

(iii) Shake the DO meter probe for better meter sensor sensitivity and take the reading on the meter.

You can repeat this two more times at different points of the pond. Then you can record the average DO readings.

[J]   Testing Pond Water Turbidity

Turbidity refers to the clarity of the water. Clear water is important in the pond because fish is able to clearly see and avoid being stressed. Turbid water is not good because fish will not be able to see resulting in stress, loss of appetite and eventually stunted growth. Follow the steps below to test for turbidity

(i)   Lower your hand into the water up to the elbow level;

(ii)   Shake or move your fingers while your hand is lowered into the water; and

(iii) If you are able to see your fingers, then the turbidity is normal and there is no cause for worry. However, if you are not able to see your fingers, then the turbidity is high and interventions are required

[K]   Pond Fertilization Using Inorganic Fertilizers

Regarding pond fertilization using inorganic fertilizers proceed as follows:

(i)   Calculate the area of the fish pond by multiplying the length and the breadth;

(ii)   Calculate the correct quantity of fertilizer by using 3grams per square meter for urea and 2grams per square meter for phosphate fertilizer. Use only one of them;

(iii)   Weigh the required quantity on a scale;

(iv)   Mix the fertilizer with water in a bucket and pour into the pond containing clear water;

(v)   After 3 to 4 days the water will turn into greenish color and the pond is fertilized.

[L]   Pond Fertilization using organic Fertilizers

Normally sawdust-free chicken manure is employed owing to its high nitrogen content. Sawdust kills fish. Regarding pond fertilization using organic fertilizers proceed as follows:

(i)   Pack the chicken manure in either 25kg or 50kg bags and tie them tightly;

(ii)   Throw the bags into the clear pond water;

(iii)   Leave them for 6 to 7 days until the water turns a greenish color thereby showing that the pond is fertilized; and

(iv)   Remove the bags out to avoid over fertilizing the pond

N.B.   Do not offload the chicken manure directly into the pond.

[M]   Liming a Pond

Regarding liming, proceed as follows:

(i)   Calculate the area of the fishpond by multiplying the length and the breadth;

(ii)   Calculate the correct quantity of lime by using 200grams per square meter;

(iii)   Weigh the required quantity on a scale; and

(iv)   Mix the lime with water in a bucket and pour into the pond usually in each of the four corners and then in the middle for easy diffusion.

[N]   Water Management

One of the critical aspects of pond management is how water quality is managed and maintained in a pond. It is required that pond water quality is maintained by ensuring that water in the pond remains fresh at all times to aid the speedy growth of the fish. Water in the natural water bodies (rivers, lakes, streams etc) is fresh at all times owing to the underground base wells on the river bed and the continuous current that sweeps away the toxic waste (ammonia, nitrates and nitrites) from the fish. Therefore, the fish farmer needs to make sure that a continuous flow of fresh water is poured into the fish pond on a daily basis to ensure better fish health and growth. If, however, the fish farmer has a challenge with water quantity, then at least he/she needs to pump fresh water into the pond twice per week. Two mechanisms are normally used here:-

[O]   Simultaneous inflow and outflow of Pond Water

This is a situation where the fish farmer will be pumping in fresh water in the pond and at the same time draining out the toxic water. This creates a current inside the pond that eventually leaves clean and clear water that the fish require. This has to be done on a daily basis for better health and growth of the fish. Please do all you can to adhere to this requirement.

[P]   Drain and Pump System

In this method, the fish farmer will first drain out half of the toxic water from the pond using the drainage system and then afterwards pump in fresh water to freshen the pond water for better fish health and survival.

[Q]   Sample Weighing the Fish & Average Body Weight (ABW)

Sample weighing of the fish is important because it helps the fish farmer to monitor the growth rate of the fish. It also helps in the calculation of feed ration (quantity of food to feed the fish per day). The following steps are normally employed during sample weighing the fish.

(i)   Scoop water from the pond whose fish you want to sample weigh;
(ii)   Weigh the water and the bucket and record the weight [Weight A]:
(iii)   Throw a little feed into the fish pond to attract the fish;
(iv)   Now throw in or cast the Cast Net in order to catch a sample of the fish in the pond;
(v)   Count the number of the fish caught and record;
(vi)   Put the caught fish in a bucket of course salt (containing water from the same pond which is inhabited ted by the fish since they are acclimatized to it);
(vii)   Weigh the fish, water and bucket and record the weight [Weight B];
(viii) Now subtract Weight A from Weight B to get the Weight of the fish;

(ix) Finally divide the Weight of the Fish by the Number of the Fish Caught to get the Average Body Weight (ABW) of one fish in the pond. This ends sample weighing which is normally done every two weeks to monitor fish growth rate.

[R] Fish Feed

The amount of feed for the fish per day (feed ration) is dependent on the average body weight of the fish. Recommended standards of feed ration are dependent on feeding charts from various Feed Manufacturing Companies. These charts show the average body weight and feeding rates necessary to calculate the feed ration. If a farmer has 100 fingerlings each weighing 6grams, calculate the feed ration assuming that feed rate is 5% of body weight.

Solution: Find total body weight for all the fish in the pond=6g x 100 fingerlings = 600grams.

5%/100% x 600grams = 30grams of feed per day. Therefore, the feed ration is 30grams per day. Dividing this quantity by 4 (feeding frequency) provides the quantity of feed at each feeding instance.

Feeding Timings: Feeding frequency varies depending on the average body weight of the fish. The farmer needs to rely on the feeding chart from the feed company. However, fish may be fed 5, 4, 3 times per day. The fish will then learn the feeding timings and would automatically come at the surface at that time.

Position of Feeding: Throw the feed around the pond to allow each fish an opportunity to feed. Throwing feed in one feeding area is not good for small ponds because the fish will jostle for the feed and in the process some fail to eat enough creating uneven growth patterns. Additionally, the fish may injure each other causing diseases and death. Therefore, during feeding in small ponds, do not throw the feed in one place but rather broadcast the feed around the pond. Nevertheless, in large ponds, feed is best broadcast in specific feeding areas sometimes using automatic feeders and tractors.

Quantity to Throw in: Throw in very small feed at a time and observe how the fish are eating. Throwing in too much feed is wrong because the feed may quickly sink at the bottom thus wasting feed. This, however, depends on type of feed. This sank feed will not be eaten by the fish but will decompose and contaminate the water.

Specific Feeding Times: Feeding timings usually depend on temperature. If the feed chart says 4 times per day, the farmer may decide to feed from 10hrs; 12hrs, 14hrs and 16hrs or he may decide to feed from 11hrs, 13hrs, 15hrs and 17hrs depending on temperature. Fish appetite is much better at higher temperatures.

Number of days to feed the fish per week: The fish are to be fed only for 6 days in a week. Leave one day without feeding. Fish needs to rest and feed on natural feed in the water. This also creates appetite and promotes good health for the fish.

Average Body Weight (ABW) = refers to the mean weight of one fish in the pond.

Daily Feed Ration (DFR) = this refers to the amount of feed the fish requires per day. This quantity is important in order to avoid under-feeding or over-feeding the fish. The formula here is: Average fish weight x feed rate (%) x total number of fish in pond.

Net Production = total biomass harvested - total biomass stocked.

Survival Percentage (%) = total number harvested/total number stocked X 100%.

Feed Conversion Ratio (FCR). This is the ratio of the amount of feed given to the fish over the weight gain of the fish during the growth period.

$$FCR = \frac{(\text{amount of feed fed (Kg)})}{(\text{total mass increase of fish in the pond (Kg)})}$$

The closer the FCR is to 1.0 the better the feed. Suitable feeds have FCR between 1.5 and 2.0. Suitable FCRs are also a factor of optimum water quality and appropriate stocking densities. FCR determines feed quality. A lower FCR implies good feed because only a little of the feed will correspond to fish growth.

The fish's feeding response depends on Palatability of the Feed and water environment. The feed's appearance, smell, texture/feel and taste helps to influence the fish's appetite. The more palatable the feed is, the better the fish response will be.

Culture (Water) Environment. The most important water quality parameters that affect feeding response in ponds are water temperature and dissolved oxygen. The warmer the water and the higher the amount of dissolved oxygen, the more active the fish will be and the better their feed consumption and FCR. Other Stressors, such as water quality variables (notably of ammonia and pH), also affect the fish's appetite.

When fish are stressed, their appetite completely drops.

Assessing Feeding Response

The attention paid by the farmer or person feeding is extremely important in assessing how much the fish actually need to be fed at each meal, or that day. In order to make this assessment, the following should be noted by the farmer during feeding:

- How fast did the fish move towards the feed and how did this reaction/behaviour compare with that at previous feedings?
- Whether or not the fish are interested in the feed?
- What the colour of the pond water is prior to feeding?
- What proportion of the fish comes to the feed?
- What the weather was a few days before, and on that day? Is (was) it rainy, windy, cold or hot?

Categories of Feed

[1] Fry mash: Feed for one month. Weigh every 2 weeks. When the fish is 15 grams stop feeding them on fry mash and commence Crumble. This may take about 1 month.

[2] Crumble: Feed them on crumble, weighing every 2 weeks. When fish is 80 grams, stop crumble and use Pre-Starter feed.

[3] Pre-starter: Feed them on pre-starter, weighing every 2 weeks. When fish is 120grams or between 120g – 150g stop pre-starter and use grower feed.

[4] Grower: Use grower feed until the fish weighs 300grams. You may sell at this stage or you may grow them further.

[5] Finisher: Feed the fish until it weighs between 400g and 600g. Thereafter, harvest and sell.

Fish Feed Companies

Examples of fish feed companies in Zambia are Pembe feeds, Skretting Feed, Farm Feed, Novatek Feeds, Tiger Feeds, Aller Aqua and many more.

Appropriate fish feed is one that does not sink quickly but rather floats more to allow the fish to eat. Tilapia is a surface feeder. Feed that sinks easily creates debris under the pond that generates ammonia and nitrates which are harmful to the fish. Generally, natural food (phytoplankton, zooplankton and algae) is sufficient to make the fish grow but may take a long time to harvest the fish. This period may even extend to one year. Farmers can also produce their own fish feed to reduce on feed costs through feed formulation.

[R]   Procedure For Feeding the Fish

It is highly recommended that you feed your fish on quality fish feed that provides them with a balanced diet. Feeding the fish is an enjoyable exercise because it provides some form of interaction with your fish. If the weather is favorable and the feed is palatable, fish literally jumps out of water in excitement during the feeding episodes. Fish require a balanced diet therefore feed your fish on quality feeds. With regard to fish feeding, proceed as follows:

(i)   Stick to the feeding times so that the fish can master the times for feeding. Feeding times are different depending on the size of fish. Refer to the feeding chart from the feed company;

(ii)   Make some specific sound or trouble the water at each of those feeding times in order to signal the fish about the feeding time;

(iii)   Throw or broadcast a little feed at a time starting from the feeding area;

(iv)   For uniform fish growth, broadcast some feed around the pond to carter for the less aggressive fish that may be scattered around the pond; and stick to the feed ration quantities, where possible, in order to avoid over-feeding or under feeding

[S]   General Pond Management

According to Lake Way (2018), tilapia does not ask for much. In fact, they only have five basic needs: clean water, oxygen, food, light and room to swim. Give your tilapia these things, and they will stay healthy and grow fast. The art of tilapia farming is to understand each of these needs, and then find a way to provide them in sufficient quantities. The problem is that each of these five needs comes with a myriad of potentially complicated questions and solutions.

Maintain Suitable Water Quality: Poor feeding and over feeding result in poor water quality by creating debris under the water resulting in more Carbon dioxide from ammonia gas.

Maintaining Suitable Water Quantity: At all times, water levels need to be kept at the maximum height and depth. This provides enough space for all fish activities (locomotion, feeding, excretion etc).

Check for pond leaks: Periodically observe the depth of the water to see whether or not water is seeping out.

New Water: Put water that you are able to drink yourself. Ensure that the water pH and temperature are within acceptable limits.

Existing Water: Usually existing water has high levels of nutrients because of fertilization, hence needs to be maintained unless it has deteriorated significantly.

Check for grass: Cut all grass around the pond because these attract snakes.

Clean the pond of any dirt: Keep the pond clear of weeds and other debri (plastics, leaves, grass etc) and other floating substances. These may block sunlight that is required by algae under the water. Algae put oxygen in the water through the process of photosynthesis. Additionally, they create healthy fish gills. Debris usually sticks into the gills and kills the fish.

Watch out for predators: Birds, snakes and water rats are the most common fish predators. You may use a Fish Pond Bird Net. (Check for availability in Livestock Services Cooperative Society at the Show grounds, Lusaka, Zambia) or you may put scare ware (flying plastics on sticks). Snakes can be controlled by using snake repellants of various forms.

Fencing the ponds: In order to keep out children and animals, ponds require fencing although this is costly for small scale farmers

Observe Fish behavior: if the fish are very active, swimming quickly and easily, it is a sign that they are healthy and all is well. If the fish are waiting on the surface of the pond; it is a sign that they are hungry and need feed. If the fish are gasping for breath at the water surface, then there is less dissolved oxygen (DO) in the pond. If the fish are showing motionless behaviour or some sluggish motion; it is a sign they are sick.

Pond Bottom Management: remove silt, debris under the pond. You may use pond wolver or oxygen aerators that will help break down this debris by chemical reaction. Debris at the bottom of the pond is harmful because it decomposes into ammonia and nitrates that affects the fish.

Sanitization: Sanitize your hands and arms before putting them into your pond water. Handy sanitizer. This helps to avoid bacteria from your hands entering into the fish pond.

Touching pond water: Always use sanitized gloves when touching the pond water.

Maintain clean conditions around ponds. Sanitize the floors of indoor areas, and sanitize the bottoms of shoes if practical. Keep separate sets of equipment, such as nets and buckets, for each pond. Adopt a colored bucket system. White for clean water and fish holding, blue for equipment and filter cleaning or carrying, and gray for toxic water carrying. Avoid conditions that cause weakened immune systems in tilapia, such as stress due to overcrowding, poor nutrition, and high levels of nitrates.

[T] **Marketing**
Depending on available fish quantities, you may engage huge wholesalers like Shoprite, Spars, Pick n Pay; Melisa, Zambeef etc. These demand huge tons of fish and consistency of supply. Smaller wholesalers are also available and have formed specialized Teams. These normally add value to the fish before it is sold. Retail selling requires hygienic fish facilities coupled with fridges. Below is a sample of the fish marketing strategies.

- Document (names, contacts, locations) all the Hotels, Lodges, Guest Houses around your area and create a database for easy marketing when fish is ready.
- Document (names, contacts, locations) all the Restaurants around your area and create a database for easy marketing when fish is ready.
- Create door to door fliers on A4 papers for distribution in the neighbourhood and road junctions. The fliers should have a special message with current contact numbers for making orders. "Don't buy tasteless frozen fish; rather buy tasty live fresh breathing fish".
- Make a special announcement in your church (Catholics, SDA, Pentecost etc) such that all congregations in that District receive the announcement verbally and on church bulletin boards and ask members to make fish orders to support a sister or brother.
- Make a fish harvest launch by inviting a distinguished Leader (Minister, member of Parliament, Mayor, Chief, Councilor etc) to launch the harvest. The leader will come with enough people to sweep the fish.
- Partner with butchery owners so that you occupy one of their empty fridges with your fish for a few days. Fish attracts more people to the butchery who eventually buy both the fish and meat.

- Enter into sustainable contracts with the chain stores (Shoprite, Spars, Pick & Pay, Choppies, Suppermarkets etc) to supply fish on a consistent basis
- The Mines (Lumwana, Kalumbila, KCM, Mopani etc)
- General selling of fish around densely populated compound markets
- Website (Online Payments and Bookings) marketing of fish
- Social Media (Facebook, WhatsApp, Twitter etc) marketing of fish
- Market your fish through Radio and Television
- Finally you can also sell your fish by creating a weekend (Saturday or Sunday) Markets in a specific place.

[U]   Fish Harvesting

N.B. Inform your Market in advance so that orders are made or buyers are found before harvesting. Commercial farmers may even launch their harvesting by inviting a top ranking official like a Minister; Counselor; a Chief or you may invite an Organization e.g Bank staff plus Television and Radio crews etc.

Requirements: include, seine (drag) nets, scoop nets, clean plastic buckets, clean source of water and clean fish storage containers. Workers must put on fish waders (waterproof overalls). Two days before harvesting, the fish must not be fed and no pond fertilization must take place to prevent odd flavors (feed smell). Fish should be checked for off flavors. Fish should be harvested during cool weather (less active). Harvesting and transportation equipment should be set up well in advance to ensure reduced stress and minimal fish mortality. Care must be taken when carrying out partial harvesting, to prevent of fish injuries. In order to harvest the fish, proceed as follows:

(i)   For Partial Harvesting: Don't drain any water: use a net (3 to 3.5 cm mesh for big fish).

(ii)   For Complete or full Harvesting:

(a) Drain part of the water and use a net;
(b) Drain all the water; and
(c) Catch all the fish and clean the fish pond bottom.

(V)   Pond Preparation for Restocking after Harvest

Several steps are required to prepare the pond for re-stocking. These include:-

(i)   Small Pond repairs: Pond liner cracks and openings should be sealed and mended while dykes should be cleaned and weak spots reinforced, cracks filled in, holes dug by crabs or rats should be filled in to avoid water seepage and prevent the dykes from collapsing. For earthen ponds, grass that grows in the pond should be removed and excess mud/silt from the pond bottom has to be removed as well.

(ii) Drying the Pond: Preparation for the next crop begins the day after the last pieces of fish have been harvested from the pond. Firstly, the pond has to be completely drained by digging small trenches towards the outlet (or the pumping pit) so that only little water puddles remain at the pond bottom. For earthen ponds, drying the pond improves availability of nutrients in the pond bottom, the mud decomposes and most pests, water insects, amphibian larvae (e.g. tadpoles) and unwanted wild fish will disappear.

(iii) Liming the Pond: if the fish pond cannot be completely dried, then use lime to disinfect the pond. Lime kills most small creatures (parasites, insects, tadpoles, etc.) which are harmful to your fish, or which might transfer diseases. All small fish have to be killed, because they can lead to overcrowding of the pond and could carry diseases that will affect your new fish. Use 500 grams of agriculture lime ($CaCO_3$) per m2. Sprinkle it over the whole pond if it is still wet or sprinkle it only over the area which has water puddles.

(W) How to Increase Your Profits

In order to increase profits, a farmer needs to do the following:-

(i) Improve pond management skills to reduce mortalities and slow growth.

(ii) Increase the fish weight to at least 500 grams or better with your own feed.

(iii) Reduce on Commercial feeds, try to use your own feed.

(iv) Avoid both under and over stocking but stock moderately.

(v) Use quality fingerlings from a reputable hatchery. Fingerlings are sometimes stunted

[X] Examination

(1) Daily Feed Ration

If a tilapia fish of 180 grams requires a ratio of 2.5% of its body weight, how much food should it be given per day? Assuming there are 1,000 fish; calculate total amount of feed?

Solution: Amount of feed to be fed per day = 180 grams x 2.5%/100% = 4.5 grams feed to be fed per fish per day, so for 1,000 fish = 4,500g (4.5kg).

(Y)   Mortalities

In fish farming you have to consider the fact that some fish will die either through diseases, damages or predators. The rule of thumb is that mortality is 10% over a period of 6 months. Therefore you will have to buy more fingerlings than the desired number of fish at harvest. Overall mortality can be 20% if you started with fry

REFERENCES

Álvaro, O. F. (2005). Best Practices for Small to Medium Scale Tilapia Aquaculture

Antti Ha⬜ nninen (2014). Production and utilization of tilapia feed in rural Zambia

Beardmore, J.A., Mair G.C., & Lewis, R.I. (2000). Monosex male production in finfish as exemplified by tilapia: applications, problems, and prospects

Celeste, Dennis, and Paulson (2014). Backyard Ponds: Guidelines for Creating & Managing Habitat for Dragonies & Damselies

Coche A.G., James F.M., & Laughlin, T (1997). Management of Fresh Water Fish Culture: Ponds and Water Practices. The training Manual

Confred G. Musuka., et al. "Fish Imports and Their Contribution towards Feeding an Ever-Growing Population in Zambia". Innovative Techniques in Agriculture 1.2 (2017): 107-115.

FAO (2014). Food and Agriculture Organization of the United Nations, Rome, Italy. http://www.fao.org/tempref/FI/CDrom/FAO_Training/FAO_Training/Gene ral/x6709e/x6709e06.htm

FAO (2018). Fishing Gear Types Seine nets. http://www.fao.org/fishery/geartype/102/en accessed on 27th September, 2018.

FAO. "The State of World Fisheries and Aquaculture 2014. Rome".

Genschick S, Kaminski AM, Kefi AS and Cole SM. (2017). Aquaculture in Zambia: An overview and evaluation of the sector's responsiveness to the needs of the poor. Penang, Malaysia: CGIAR Research Program on Fish Agri-Food Systems and Lusaka, Zambia: Department of Fisheries. Working Paper: FISH-2017-08.

Genschick S, Kaminski AM, Kefi AS and Cole SM. (2017). Aquaculture in Zambia: An overview and evaluation of the sector's responsiveness to the needs of the poor. Penang, Malaysia: CGIAR Research Program on Fish Agri-Food Systems and Lusaka, Zambia: Department of Fisheries. Working Paper: FISH-2017-08.

Getu A, Misganaw K, Bazezew M (2015) Post-harvesting and Major Related Problems of Fish Production. Fish Aquac J 6:154. doi:10.4172/2150-3508.1000154

Gianluigi, N. (2013). Tilapia Farming Guide. NPH Haiti/Foundazione Rava

Haambiya, L; et al (2015). Local-Scale Governance: A Review of the Zambian Approach to Fisheries Management . Journal of Agricultural Science and Technology B 5 (2015)

Inland Water Resources and Aquaculture Service of the FAO (2006). Simple methods for aquaculture. Version 2. Handbook on small- scale freshwater fish culture (2nd ed). Food and Agriculture Organization of the United Nations, Rome

International Labor Organization (ILO). 2014. Analysis of the Market Systems Underpinning the Fish Value Chain in Zambia. A study carried out by the World Fish (Zambia) for ILO. Lusaka, Zambia: ILO.

Karki, P.N. (2016). Fish farming in Nepal: trends, opportunities and challenges. Nepalese Journal of Agricultural Sciences

L' Heureux, R. (1985). Economic feasibility of fish culture in Zambia. TCP/ZAM/4405

Lakeway Tilapia (2018). Tilapia farming guide - Part 1 https://lakewaytilapia.com/How_To_Raise_Tilapia.php. Accessed 28th September, 2018

mith, M. A., and Leigh, B. (1997) Virtual subjects: using the internet as an alternative source of subjects and research environment. Behaviour Research Methods, Instruments & Computers, 29, p.496

Mudenda, H.G. (2013). Commercial Aquaculture in Zambia

Mzengereza K,. and Kangombe J. (2016). Effect of dietary salt supplementation on growth, survival and feed utilization of tilapia. University of Malawi

Ngueku (2014). Water monitoring in fish ponds. International Journal of Fisheries and Aquatic Studies 2014; 2(3): 31-32

Omofunmi, O.E. (2016). Basic and Technical Considerations on Pond Design and Construction. British Journal of Applied Science & Technology 15(4): 1-10

Perry L, (2011). Aeration of ponds used in aquaculture. Agricultural engineering technical note no. aen-3

Riche, M. & Gargling, D. (2003). Feeding Tilapia in Intensive Recirculating Systems. Northern Central Regional Aquaculture Center. Retrieved April 24, 2018, from http://aquanic.org/publicat/usda_rac/efs/ncrac/ncrac114.pdf

Sale, J. E. M., Lohfeld, L. H., & Brazil, K. (2002). Revisiting the quantitative-qualitative debate: Implications for mixed-methods research. Quality and Quantity, 36(1), 43-53.

Sameer, H., Farah, N., Hanis, B., Hadi, A., Jamaludin, I. (2016). Issues and Security

Measures of Mobile Banking Apps. International Journal of Scientific and Research Publications, 6(1).

Schein, E. H. (1971). The Individual, the Organization, and the Career: A Conceptual Scheme. Journal of Applied Behavioral Science, 7, 401-426.

Scholasticus, K. (2011). History of Internet Banking

Selina, O., & Oruth, J. (2012). Enhanced ATM Security System Using Biometrics. International Journal of Computer Science Issues, 9(5), 3.

Sharmin, R. D., & Subhra, P. P. (2013). Proposed Methods of IP Spoofing Detection and Prevention. International Journal of Science and Research, 2(1)

Sidden, K., & Simmons, D. (2005). Banking on security. American City & County, 30 (11), 120.

Soma et al (1999). Analysis of fish culture in Zambia. Japan International Cooperation Agency (JICA).

Timmons, M.B., Ebeling, J.M., Wheaton, F.W., Summerfelt, F.W. and Vinci, B.J. (2001). Recirculating Aquaculture Systems. NRAC Publication No. 01 – 002. New York: North Eastern Regional Aquaculture Center.

Trilateral Tilapia Cooperative Project. (2014). State Department of Fisheries. Ministry of Agriculture, Livestock and Fisheries, Nairobi, Kenya.

Waples, R.S., and C. Do. (1994). Genetic risk associated with supplementation of Pacific salmonids: Captive broodstock programs. Canadian Journal of Fisheries and Aquatic Science, 51(1), 310–329.

Wikipedia (2018). Seining for fish in a river. Accessed: 28th September, 2018. https://en.wikipedia.org/wiki/Seine_fishing

Wokoma M and Ezenwa C. (2001). Construction of brackish water fish pond in Niger Delta. University of Port Harcourt. Nigeria. NIOMR Technical Paper. 2001;23(4):4–10

Zambia Development Agency (2011). Ministry of Livestock and Fisheries. Sector Report

APPENDICES

Appendix 1. Average Body Weight (ABW) and Feeding Rate

FEED TYPE	ABW (g)	FEEDING RATE	FEEDING FREQ
Fry Mash	0.5 – 1.5g	12%	5X
Fry Mash	1.5 – 5.0g	10%	4X
Fry Mash	5.0 – 15g	6.5%	4X
Fingerling Meal	15 – 30g	6.0%	4X
Fingerling Meal	30 – 80g	5.0%	3X
Juvenile	80 – 120g	4.0%	3X
Juvenile	120 – 200g	3.0%	3X
Juvenile	200 – 300g	2.5%	3X
Juvenile/Green Pond	300g Upwards	2.0%	2.3X

Appendix 2. Quantity of Feed at each Feeding Time

FEEDING FREQUENCY	FEEDING TIMINGS & PERCENTAGE OF FEED AT EACH TIME				
5X	8hrs 0.5%	10hrs 15%	12hrs 30%	14hrs 30%	16hrs 20%
4X	10hrs 20%	12hrs 30%	14hrs 30%	16hrs 30%	
3X	10hrs 20%	14hrs 40%	16hrs 40%		
2X	10-12hrs 40%		14-15hrs 60%		

Appendix 3. Pond Management Record

Pond Record	Possible Causes	What should I do?

Appendix 4. Mortality Chart

Pond 1	Date	Mortality Number	Possible Cause	Intervention

Appendix 5. Total Number of Feed [Bags] Kgs Used

Name of Pond	Fry Mash	Crumble	Pre-Starter	Grower	Finisher
	Total # of bags Kgs	Total # of bags Kgs	Total # of bags Kgs	Total # of bags Kgs	Total # of bags Kgs

Appendix 6. Average Body Weight (ABW) Sample Weighing

DATE	Weeks (every two weeks)	Average Body Weight (g)	Comments on Growth Rates and Interventions
	Week 2		
	Week 4		
	Week 6		
	Week 8		
	Week 10		

N.B. You can also measure ABW every month using a Seine (Drag) Net. This is good because you will be able to see the fish sizes at once

Appendix 7. Fish Pond Water Quality Measurements

DATE	pH	Dissolved Oxygen	Temp	Turbidity	Waste Products (Ammonia/Nitra tes/Nitrite s)	Comments on Growth Rates and Interventions

Appendix 8. Feeding Schedule

DATE	Type of Feed	Feed Quantity	Number of Feeding Times	Observation (Fish Response & Explanation)

Appendix 9. Common Bacterial Tilapia Fish Diseases

Common Bacterial Tilapia Diseases	Causes	Symptoms	Preventive measure & Cure
Fin Rot, which is sometimes called Tail Rot, is a very common bacterial disease affecting fish in ponds. Typically, this disease starts around the edges of the fin and gradually destroys more tissue until it reaches the base of the fin.	Fin Rot is caused by different types of gram-negative bacteria which include Aeromonas, Pseudomonas fluorescens, and Vibrio. These organisms eat away at the membranes of the fins, leaving them ragged and frayed. The damaged and frayed tissue is then vulnerable to secondary fungal infections. The biggest cause of Fin Rot is poor water quality (poor water environment which allows bacteria to thrive.	Symptoms of Fin Rot include inflamed patches on the fins, discoloration on the edges of the fins, and fraying of the fin or tail. Other symptoms include lethargy and loss of appetite.	Improve the water quality in the fish pond. This will include a complete changing of existing water. After this, you can measure the pH and dissolved oxygen levels of the new water. You can also include course salt to the water to help treat the infection, soothe the fish, and prevent infections in the future. Don't over feed and overstock the pond. Aggressive fish sometimes damages the fins of other fish which may result in risk of infection
streptococcosis	streptococcus agalactiae is the main cause of streptococcosis in farmed tilapia. Other bacteria that may cause this tilapia disease include Streptococcus iniae; Streptococcus dysagalactiae and Lactococcus garviae

Risk factors include very high temperatures (31-33 oC); poor water quality and low oxygenation | external haemorrhages.

endophthalmia or exophthalmia (popped-up eyes)

Unilateral or bilateral opacification of the eye

eye haemorrhages

erratic swimming darkening lost of appetite

Abscesses in the inferior jaw and pectoral fins

swirling behaviour, lethargy, bent bodies and disorientation of fish are commonly | Improve water quality Control water temperature by increasing water level in the pond

Aerate the pond for more oxygen

Improve fish immunity by relying on vitamin C enriched feed |

| Columnaris | Caused by bacteria Flavobacterium Columnare a gram negative, rod-shaped bacterium. | One of the first symptoms of columnaris in tilapia is usually frayed and ragged fins. Another early warning sign is brown or yellowish-brown lesions that appear on the skin, the mouth, the fins and the gills of the fish. Gills usually become darkened, yellowish or dark red | Stress is a major cause of columnaris in tilapia fish. Remove all elements that cause stress in fish. Maintain water quality, water chemistry, oxygen levels and water temperature within the recommended ranges, feed your fish a suitable diet and avoid overcrowding. Flavobacterium columnare thrives |

Appendix 10. Common Tilapia Species in Zambia

Tilapia Species	Characteristics
OREOCHROMIS NILOTICUS	Tilapia Niloticus, a cichlid native to North Africa/Israel, has a slightly grayish whitish colour, distinctive, regular, vertical stripes extending as far down the body as the bottom edge of the caudal fin, with variable coloration. Adults reach up to 60cm in length and up to 4.3 kg. It lives for up to nine years. It is an aggressive and highly invasive specie. Nile tilapia is primarily herbivorous, with aquatic macrophytes, algae, and diatoms generally comprising >90% of its diet and the remainder including aquatic insects and crustaceans and fish eggs (Khallaf and Alne-na-ei 1987). It is fast-growing and tolerant of a range of environmental conditions. These species adapt readily to changes in salinity levels and oxygen availability and can feed at different trophic levels. Owing to its invasive nature, some countries restrict its stocking to certain regions only.
OREOCHROMIS ANDERSONII	Oreochromis andersonii, the three-spotted tilapia, threespot tilapia, or threespot bream, is a species of cichlid native to Africa, where it is found in rivers and swamps in the southern half of the continent. This species reaches a length of 61 cm (24 in) and can grow up to 4.7 Kg and can live up to 13 years. Most common pond fish in Zambia. Grows at 1.5g per day in optimum environments depending on stocking density and suitable water environment. Experiments have shown that it can outgrow Niloticus at certain altitudes.
OREOCHROMIS MACROCHIR	Oreochromis macrochir is a species of cichlid native to the Zambezi Basin, Lake Mweru, and Lake Bangweulu. It has been used extensively for stocking ponds and dams in other parts of southern Africa, but is little-used elsewhere. In Lake Mweru, it is economically the most important fish. It is sometimes called a green-headed bream and has long fins. It can grow up to 43cm and 5kg weight. Prefers quiet, deep water associated with aquatic vegetation and enjoys temperatures between 18 and 35°C. It has a very low salinity tolerance and occasionally forms schools, is mainly diurnal. Feeds mostly on detritus. Can grow at 0.9g per day
OREOCHROMIS RENDALLI	It is sometimes called a redbreast tilapia. Redbreast tilapia is generally an omnivorous, opportunistic feeder throughout its life. Largely herbivorous, it is deep-bodied with a convex forehead profile. Females have red chests and up to nine vertical bands. Males have white chests. Red breast tilapia often have a distinct two-tone caudal fin colouration, red at the base and pale above, with no spotting. They are robust-bodied and will jump when surprised. This is the tastiest tilapia, but it grows slowly. The species is popular in aquaponics as it consumes plant waste. Temperature tolerance between 14°C Chervinski, 1982). It can tolerate fairly brackish salinities

Appendix 11. Costing and Income

Costing a fish pond is fairly easy and involves three or two levels depending on one's costing preferences. These levels are Cost of Construction; Cost of Production and Cost of Accessories. Others compress the Cost of Production and Cost of Accessories into Cost of Production only.

i) **COST OF CONSTRUCTION**

Define the type of fish pond (earthen, lined or concrete)
Define the Size of your fish pond
Define your Stocking density
Define the number of fingerlings to stock
Cost of borehole
Cost of submersible pump and accompanying accessories
Cost of polypipes for transporting water to the fish pond
Cost of tanks (if necessary)
Cost of Power (solar/electricity/generator/wind)
Cost of Pond (Digging) Excavation
Cost of Pond Liners (in the case of a lined pond)
Cost of lining the Pond liners inside the pond
Cost of inlet construction
Cost of outlet construction
Sub-Total Construction

ii) **COST OF PRODUCTION**

Cost of Fingerlings (buy from reputable hatcheries/nurseries)
Cost of Feed for 6 Months (use quality feed for better growth)
Feed Conversion Ratio (FCR)
Cost of agricultural lime
Cost of inorganic fertilisers (urea and/or phosphate)

[You can also use organic fertilisers esp. chicken manure]
Running cost for power pertaining to fish farming business
Cost of transportation/fuel
Cost of Airtime pertaining to fish farming business
Cost of labour in 6 months

Cost of a Digital Scale
Cost of Course Salt
Cost of water quality measuring instruments (pH Meter, Dissolved Oxygen, Temperature, Ammonia/Nitrates and Turbidity)
Cost of plastic buckets and dishes
Cost of Pond Liner Welder
Cost of Pond Liner Gun
Cost of Cast Net
Cost of Seine Net
Cost for dissolved oxygen aerators
Sub-Total Production

Final Total = Sub-total Construct + Sub-Total Production

N.B. Note that most of these items will be acquired in subsequent years as you expand your fish farming business. Some of the items are one-off which maybe required only once per production cycle and fish farmers normally borrow such items from each other. Additionally items like source of power, boreholes and submersible pumps may already exist on the farm. The cheapest ponds to construct are earthen ponds. In cases where the source water is from a natural water body (river, lakes, dams, streams etc), construction of the pond may be much cheaper owing to less investment in the water supply mechanism. For concrete ponds, you need to see a bricklayer for better costing.

PROFIT CALCULATIONS

Size of your fish pond e.g.	50 x 25
Fish Pond Area	1,250 m^2
Stocking Density	5 fingerlings/m^2
Number of fish stocked	6,250
Average Body Weight @ harvest	400g
Calculate Pond Biomas[P]	2,500kgs
Determine your wholesale price [Q]	K27.00/Kg

Calculate Income [O] Thus O = P X Q and convert from grams into kgs or tons K67,500.00

N.B. The income figure may go up if you consider weighing all the fish in the pond. This is because the extra 10% given when purchasing fingerlings has not been factored in. Additionally, most of the fish may well be above the Average Body Weight of 400g. Profit is then calculated by subtracting the total expenditure in the 6 months culture period from the income. The first harvest normally results in a loss owing to many factors notable among which is the heavy investments in fish farming infrastructure. Profits are realized from the second harvest onwards with careful adoption of best management practices.

Appendix 12. Practical Fish Farming Training Companies in Zambia

Breathing Fish Farm Behind
Westwood Police Station
Mumbwa Road, Chilanga, Zambia.
Service: Fish Farming Training
Contact : +260-978-751050
E-mail :   collinschi@gmail.com

Palabana Fisheries
HQ Sub 15 of Sub B of Farm 380a
Chongwe, Zambia.
Service: Fish Farming Training
Contact: +260-977-822-030

IBAN AQUAFISH Solutions & Consultancy Limited
Stand Number F29, Lusaka. Showgrounds Lusaka. Zambia
Service: Fish Farming Training
Contact : +260-977-767-456; +260-966-300-124
E-mail : iban.aquafish@gmail.com

Appendix 13. Names of Fish Feed Companies in Zambia

Farmfeed Limited
Mukwa Road, Lusaka, Zambia.
Products : Tilapia Frymash, Tilapia 35, Green Pond Feed
Custom mixes to suit farmer's needs
Contact Numbers: +260-966-665-480
E-mail Address :   peter.farmfeed@gmail.com

Novatek Animal Feeds
Zambia's largest stock feeds producer
Producers of fish feeds
Contact: Aquaculture Manager
Contact Numbers: +260-971-252-522; +260-968-481-564
E-mail Address: fish.ta@novatek.co.zm

Aller Aqua Zambia Limited
6981 Mukwa Road, Lusaka, Zambia.
Product : Fish Feed
Website : www.aller-aqua.co.zm
Contact Numbers: +260-968-829-425; +260-211-243-003
E-mail Address : ln@aller-aqua.co.zm

IBAN AQUAFISH Solutions & Consultancy Limited
Stand Number F29, Lusaka. Showgrounds Lusaka. Zambia
Product : Fish Feed
Contact : +260-977-767-456; +260-966-300-124
E-mail : iban.aquafish@gmail.com

Skretting Zambia Limited (A Nutreco Company)
Farm Number.9074
P.O. Box 23, Siavonga, Zambia
Product : Fish Feed
Contact: +260-211-391-009; +260-976-258-187
Website : www.skretting.com
E-mail: sikabalu.malawo@skretting.com

Appendix 14. Fingerings Sources in Zambia

Palabana Fisheries
HQ Sub 15 of Sub B of Farm 380a
Chongwe, Zambia.
Product: Fingerlings
Contact: +260-977-822-030

Chirundu Breams Farm Limited
Plot 9265, Chirundu 6Km from Chirundu Boarder
Product: Tilapia oreochromis Niloticus Fingerlings
Contact: +260-977-785-613; +260-964-205-487; +260-969-984-121

Msekese Fisheries, Chilanga, Zambia
Product: Tilapia oreochromis Andersonii Fingerlings
Contact: +260-962-050-47

First Hatch; Showgrounds, Lusaka, Zambia.
Product : Fingerlings
Contacts: +260-977-923-425; +260-955-545-295

Yalelo Fisheries through Horizons
Product : Fingerlings
Contact: +260-979-415-130

Nsomba Yathu, Shimabala, Chilanga, Zambia.
Product : Fingerlings and Table Size Fish
Contacts: +260-966-242-198

Beltesmol Fisheries Enterprises
Situated in Siavonga District
Along Lakeshore, Matinangala
Product : Fingerlings
Contact: +260-979-142-415; +260-967-152-416
E-mail : fwanyangms@gmail.com

IBAN AQUAFISH Solutions & Consultancy Limited
Stand Number F29, Lusaka. Showgrounds Lusaka. Zambia
Product : fingerlings
Contact : +260-977-767-456; +260-966-300-124
E-mail : iban.aquafish@gmail.com

Appendix 15. Pond Liner Suppliers in Zambia

Hams Trade Limited
Shop No.3, Katondo Street. P.O. Box FW161, Lusaka, Zambia.
Product : Pond Liners and other Aquaculture Products
Contact : +260-977-343-881; +260-955-906-585
E-mail : harryalvin2006@yahoo.com; hamtrade@zamnet.zm

Breathing Fish Farm
Behind Westwood Police Station
Mumbwa Road, Chilanga, Zambia.
Product : Pond Liners and other Aquaculture Products
Contact : +260-978-751050
E-mail : collinschi@gmail.com

IBAN AQUAFISH Solutions & Consultancy Limited
Stand Number F29, Lusaka. Showgrounds Lusaka. Zambia

Product : Pond Liners and other Aquaculture Products
Contact : +260-977-767-456; +260-966-300-124
E-mail : iban.aquafish@gmail.com

Palabana Fisheries
HQ Sub 15 of Sub B of Farm 380a
Chongwe, Zambia.
Product : Pond Liners and other Aquaculture Products
Contact: +260-977-822-030

Msekese Fisheries, Chilanga, Zambia
Product : Pond Liners and other Aquaculture Products
Contact: +260-964-994-353

First Hatch; Showgrounds, Lusaka, Zambia.
Product : Pond Liners and other Aquaculture Products
Contacts: +260-977-923-425; +260-955-545-295

Appendix 16. Table Size Fish Producers

Chifwema Fisheries
Near Chifwema Primary School
P.O. Box 34567, Chifwema Road, Lusaka, Zambia.
Product : table size fish
Contacts : +260-977-750-240; +260-976-310-050

Shemma Lakes Fisheries
Chifunabuli District, Luapula Province, Zambia.
Product : table size fish
Contacts : +260-977-772-585

First Hatch; Showgrounds, Lusaka, Zambia.
Product : table size fish
Contacts: +260-977-923-425; +260-955-545-295

Breathing Fish Farm
Behind Westwood Police Station
Mumbwa Road, Chilanga, Zambia.

Product : table size live fish
Contact : +260-978-751050
E-mail : collinschi@gmail.com

Nsomba Yathu, Shimabala, Chilanga, Zambia.
Product : table size fish
Contacts: +260-966-242-198

Appendix 17. Social and Fishing Sports Companies in Zambia

Chifwema Fisheries
Near Chifwema Primary School
P.O. Box 34567, Chifwema Road, Lusaka, Zambia.
Product : Outdoor social fishing, angling, fish and grab, braai and camping
Contacts : +260-977-750-240; +260-976-310-050

Appendix 18. SADC Fish Companies

McVISE Aquaculture Consultancy
6 Natalie Road, Woodville Park, Bulawayo, Zimbabwe.
Products & Services: Pond Construction; Fingerlings; pond liners; Cage Construction; Fish
Farming Training; Rafter Boat Construction; Hatchery Construction; Aquaculture Project Management; Fish Medication; fish equipment and all.

Appendix 19. Fish Pond Billboard

This billboard is normally erected on each pond and should contain the following information:-

Name of the Pond
Stocking Date
Stocking Density
Number of Fingerlings Stocked
Name of Fish Species Stocked
Weight of fingerlings @ stocking
Current Weight of Fish @ Sampling Date

N.B. This information is also written in the Pond Book

Made in the USA
Coppell, TX
09 July 2021